Freddy Stringer

Flying Boffin

Freddy Stringer

Flying Boffin

F.S. STRINGER

B.Sc., FRIN, C. Eng., FRAeS, FRSA

Air Research Publications

First published 2005.
Air Research Publications
PO Box 223, Walton-on-Thames,
Surrey, KT12 3YQ
England

Printed in England by
Cromwell Press, Wiltshire.

ISBN 1-871187-49-4

FOREWORD

It is rare but not unusual for a scientist to be a pilot, but it is certainly unusual for the two qualities to be coupled with a very competent artist. Moreover, coupled with an artist who paints aircraft to look as though they actually fly. That, in itself, is sadly a rare skill.

'Flying Boffin' is a first-class account of the life of a remarkable man. After all, he is still flying as an instructor in his 80's! But what astonishes me is his incredible memory and his surprising stock of what I would term documentary evidence.

Freddy followed a career not greatly dissimilar from my own. During 41 years in The Royal Air Force, particularly in the latter half, I was much concerned with the technical aspects of aviation. The Royal Aircraft Establishment at Farnborough – Freddy's temple, so to speak – played a large part in my life. I therefore found 'Flying Boffin' a most interesting and fascinating book, at times very nostalgic.

It is always a pleasure to read of the life of someone who unashamedly enjoyed his work and life in general.

Neil Wheeler

Air Chief Marshal Sir Neil Wheeler
GCB CBE DSO DFC* AFC FRAeS

Dedicated to my darling Renée whose never failing love and support made everything possible and such fun. She died when this book was partly complete in 1995, but she laughed at some of the exploits in the early chapters. We shared many of them.

A superior aviator is one who uses his superior knowledge and judgement to avoid flying in conditions which require his superior skill

ACKNOWLEDGEMENTS

My thanks and acknowledgements are due to all of my colleagues but especially to Renée for her encouragement to write the book. Also to Jenny Handscombe who gave me the spur to get on and complete it.

To Mike Bagshaw for all the teaching and care, to the late Ron Campbell who provided such wisdom in things aviation.

Thanks are also due to the Downing Street Studios, Farnham, who photographed some of my paintings.

For the patience and persistence of Anne and Anna at Focus Secretarial Services for typing and putting the text and illustrations on disc. To Helen and Geoff of Genesis Fine Arts who have been so helpful.

Lastly to all my colleagues in the wide world of aviation in the United Kingdom and particularly in the United States of America.

CONTENTS

APPENDICES

ILLUSTRATIONS

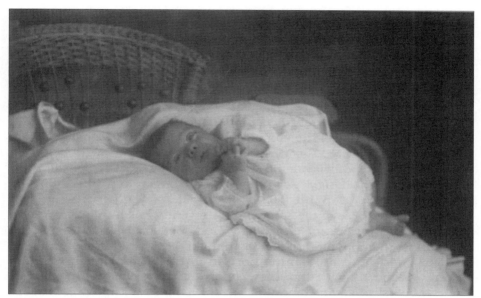

i - Baby Freddy - age six weeks.

ii - Freddy - age sixty.

Chapter 1

SNAPPER BRAT

I was born in married quarters just outside Victoria Barracks, Beverley on 15th June 1922, the son of the then Regimental Sergeant Major Fred Stringer MSM. My father served in the East Yorkshire Regiment of the British Army for some 36 years having joined as a boy volunteer at the age of 12, taking regular service as a bugler at 15 in 1906. He rose from bugler to RSM in 10 years, an astounding performance. My grandfather was also of the same regiment retiring as a colour sergeant. The three of us were all christened Fred, not Frederick, a cause for constant correction to those who thought and still think that Fred must be short for a full name. Born in Sheffield, my father's military career was mostly with the East Yorks, the 15th of Foot, nicknamed 'the Snappers' to commemorate a victory against Washington's troops during the American War of Independence when, having run out of ball ammunition, the troops fired their muskets with explosive charges only, known as 'snapping', to win the day.

My father did well; he became a crack shot in that peacetime "Contemptible Little Army" as Kaiser Bill called it, rising through the ranks with service around the British Isles in a variety of roles. At one time, serving with the First Battalion, he became a horseman in that strange unit known as the mounted infantry. These soldiers were not cavalry. They rode as a rapid means of transport and dismounted before going into action. At the outbreak of World War I in August 1914 he was a senior non-commissioned officer but did not go straight to France with the British Expeditionary Force; he remained in England to train a new Battalion, the 6th (Pioneer) Battalion East Yorks Regiment. These fighting troops had the unenviable task of preparing trenches, roads, other defences and fighting as infantry as required. They were ready for action by 1915 and sailed for Egypt, Mudros and Salonika and were blooded in August of that year in the dreadful Gallipoli campaign, landing at Suvla Bay. The Anzacs had landed further east in April. Casualties were comparatively light during the initial landing with lighters ferrying the troops from the heavy transports out in the Bay. The Battalion dug in some several hundred yards inland as ordered. They waited for the order to advance. None came. At daybreak they watched the Turks reinforcements bombard our trenches with shellfire causing heavy British casualties. The 6th Battalion did advance later and took the most advanced position of the expedition at Tel el Kepi. It was during this action that Lt.Col. Cowper O.C. of the Battalion was captured, then bayoneted to death in cold blood.

I retain a pencil written diary of those days compiled on the spot. The heat, flies, disease and carnage with shelter snatched in the rock and sand must have been unbearable. As Regimental Quartermaster Sergeant, my father had the Herculean task of feeding and supplying stores, clothing and ammunition to the Battalion. An interesting coincidence of war was that his brother Jim was in the same unit. Many books have recorded the part played by the regiment on Gallipoli but personal stories have a special ring to them. I recall one or two. One officer wore a nightshirt despite the situation. He was mistaken for a Turk one night and a flash rumour spread that the enemy had broken through our lines. Pandemonium reigned for a while until the truth dawned.

Though such a champion shot, my father always fired left handed though normally right handed in every other respect. The reason was that as a child he had been scalded causing damage to his right eye. He did not see so well with it. At one stage when we were in Catterick Camp, he obtained and sometimes wore a monocle, but I never saw him with it outside. It was during the heat of the Gallipoli fighting that officialdom decided that he should have a medical. Having avoided any argument with the medics about his eyesight over the years, it was at this incongruous stage that doubts were expressed as to this fitness. He suggested a return home. This received the expected answer in the negative. Instead he was promoted Regimental Sergeant Major at the age of 24 in charge of 1200 men!

On parade in Egypt after the evacuation of Gallipoli, he found that drilling the whole battalion required an enormous vocal effort, the sand absorbed the sound of his voice. He taught me later that when I became a School Cadet RSM to shout from the stomach. My uncle Jim concluded that his experiences on Gallipoli were enough and he volunteered for the Royal Flying Corps as pilot, for a more equitable life. He subsequently trained in England, joined 13 Squadron in France flying BE2c and RE8 army cooperation aircraft. He shot down an Albatross DIII and his observer another, but was eventually overcome himself by twelve Fokker DVII fighters which followed him down to a crash landing in no-mans land where he was captured and spent the rest of his war as a POW. His life was saved by spinning out of the German field of fire, but his spin recovery was late and a crash landing was inevitable. The RE8 was a pretty lethal aircraft in this respect, in fact so many trainees were killed as a result of spinning that the types used for conversion training were provided with a larger fin area to improve spin recovery, but at the expense of overall performance. He told me that his instrument panel disintegrated under the enemy fire and after hitting the ground 'Jerry' kept shooting him up. He stumbled away from the wreckage convinced that his gunner was dead, but he was more than a little surprised to find the lad running with him, unfortunately into a trench and the wrong end of a German Luger pistol. He died at Oulton Broad near Lowestoft in 1980.

13

My father went on to France in time for the first Battle of the Somme on 1 July 1916 when the British Army suffered such terrible casualties. He was to suffer the appalling quagmire of Paschendale and altogether, was present in one way or another in 32 engagements in the 'war to end wars'.

His experiences were such that for years he would have dreams and nightmares waking us up as a family in the night with shouts in his sleep.

Once a shell landed under his horse's legs but did not explode in the mud. On another occasion, his batman, a released convict, 'found' him a bottle of champagne when the Battalion was resting in tents just behind the lines. He got down on his camp bed and drank the whole bottle then went to sleep. He was awakened by the batman who said he was amazed to find 'Sir' still alive. A shell had landed just beside the tent but the blast had gone upwards. Dad had not been disturbed, it was obviously good champagne.

Awaiting the attack at the start of Messines Ridge, while enormous land mines were exploded by the British under the German trenches, he dozed off with his respirator (gas mask) on. He awoke to see the earth rising in front of him as the mines went up wondering where he was, with the respirator over his head and all. He was awarded the Meritorious Service Medal for his part in that engagement and was later mentioned in Despatches.

The 6th Battalion was disbanded at the end of the 1914 -1918 war and being a regular soldier, my father was posted as RSM to the Depot in Beverley. He was to be an RSM for 12 years. The main reason for this was the disbanding of the Irish regiments in 1922 and the drafting in of many regulars to other line infantry, absorbing potential vacancies for promotion.

It was in Beverley that my mother Ellen came on the scene. Their romance culminated in marriage in July 1921. Ellen Bell was the tenth of twelve children. Her father owned North Sea trawlers at Hull where she was born. He brought his bride, Betina, from Norway aged 16, Samuel Bell, Ellen's father, died early and the family moved from Hull to Beverley. Grandma Bell died there in 1936 at the age of 82, still with a strong Norwegian accent.

My second name, Samuel, was no doubt of my mother's wish in his memory. One of my twin grandsons is also a Samuel. Betina Bell lived for many years at 2 Well Lane, Beverley, a small cottage demolished circa 1965 and replaced by two garages. I recall that it was a two-room cottage, downstairs was coloured white (whitewash) and had a small backyard with a water pump of the old manual type for supply of fresh water.

I arrived on the scene in the RSM's quarter in the following June, delivered by Dr Munro, a local civilian doctor. My earliest recollections surrounded that building which still stands, although the barracks was demolished in 1983, just 99 years after being built for Queen Victoria's Army upon its reorganisation by Lord Cardwell. We had a regular batman at all times, ostensibly to look after my father, but the duties included a variety of domestic chores, not the least keeping an eye on me and later on my brother, Ivor. Names such as Carling, Pollard, Hardy and others were soldiers who enjoyed this partial relief from peacetime soldiering. Also Shields later on – my Mum liked him. I also had one or two nursemaids over those early years. None of the attention and schooling however, prevented me from becoming what some must have regarded as a bloody nuisance at times. Mrs Foster, a lady who remembered me at the time, told my wife Renée many years later that I was the 'scourge of the Depot' as a youngster.

I suppose that some recalled incidents added credence to her dubious accolade. For instance the regiment was periodically visited by the local beagle pack. The meet would move off from the parade ground, through the gate in the wall to the training and sports field at the back of the Depot and thence to the East Yorkshire countryside. At the age of just under 5, I decided to follow the pack, persuading several of my young friends from the 'married patch' to join me. My team of tots soon lost the pack and adult followers, and tears began to fall as I realised we were lost. However I managed to lead them all home via a field full of quizzical cows and round the edge of a chalk pit, but on arrival copped hell, my father had turned out the troops to look for us!

The regimental badminton match was severely disrupted when I jammed a racquet press over my head. The match had to stop while players took turns to pull it off, accompanied by loud howls from the RMS's eldest. We moved into a new quarter in the barracks itself in 1926; it was a flat above the schoolroom where I followed in my father's footsteps, learning my three Rs in the very same place as he had before. An academic career seemed forecast as I became the first in the class to progress to the three times table.

Experimental methods were also foreshadowed when I tried to flush the cat down the lavatory to see if it was feasible. Our batman, Pollard, rescued the poor thing. Funny, but I am now an ardent cat lover, indeed I love nearly all animals. The ginger female cat presented us with a litter of kittens, but fell out of favour after a spring clean of the quarter. Pollard smelt something suspicious and moved the piano to find the cat had left its card. He grabbed her and wiped her face in it as a future deterrent. Pussy then ran onto the parade ground alongside our building where recruits were drilling. Two officers were talking to each other in front of the squads and they were obviously unaware that the friendly cat with tail upright was not rubbing their legs in affection but actually wiping her face clean on their puttees.

My parents and I were invited to tea by the Commanding Officer, Major Bray, and his wife. The children were sent to play in the nursery. Apparently I suggested a game of soldiers and found a tin utensil under the bed, it made a fine helmet. My adversary found that his toy sword would not dent the pot, but once again I had something jammed on my head; niceties of formal afternoon tea were embarrassingly interrupted while the offending article was removed from the howling offspring once more.

My brother, Ivor, arrived on 15th March 1925 and he turned out to be a much better behaved lad. He grew up to have great talents as a research chemist with the Esso Company having previously spent a very rough World War II as a member of the 75th Anti-Tank Regiment in the 11th Armoured Division. From Normandy to Luneberg Heath, his unit was a spearhead of the British 2nd Army fighting in Europe. He was demobbed as a Sergeant in the Royal Artillery after the War. His soldier-like fortitude stood him well in recent years as he recovered from serious cerebral surgery, but he died of brain cancer in 1998.

My father was commissioned Lieutenant and Quartermaster on 15th October 1927. He said that 10 shillings would go to the first soldier to salute him. This was not so simple as one would suspect since the RSM's uniform differed little from that of an officer and the Depot staff and recruits were used to seeing him daily anyway. However, he was noticed and the soldier got his ten bob, a princely sum considering that a private's pay was only 2 shillings or so a day.

The commission meant a posting, so we proceeded by train to Aldershot and the 2nd Battalion.

We arrived at Mandora Barracks to be met at the very large QM's quarter, Mandora Lodge, by a new batman kitted out with a thin striped blue and white mess jacket. He had laid tea for us and the sight of a large polished dining room table with four large issue cups and saucers at each side staggered even me as a five year old. One cup was for my brother, only 2½. RQMS, Micky Bowden, joined us later and as I looked out of the window I saw three aircraft flying in formation, obviously from Farnborough and probably No. 4 Squadron Bristol Fighters. I had never seen so many aircraft together before; my mother said that I would see a lot more of them in the future; a prophetic statement indeed.

In Beverley I had often run to the children's playground swing to get nearer to any aircraft flying over, probably from Brough so I was delighted to see low flying aircraft over the barracks in Aldershot and can still recall their profile, one distinctly being a Handley Page Hydrabad and another, a Fairy Fawn, with a man leaning out of the rear cockpit of the latter winding a cine camera by hand.

Life at Aldershot was fun. There was a lot more activity than in Beverley, many more soldiers, the excitement of the band and drums, but above all, the Tattoo on Rushmoor Arena. Miss Seed's school for officers' children in Knolly's Road was held on mornings only, but once a year we stayed for a packed lunch then attended the daylight matinees. We were fortunate indeed because we were also allowed to stay up late to watch

iii - Mandora Barracks, Aldershot, 1929. Dad with Ivor, on our swing, and Freddy.

the searchlight Tattoo proper. Rushmoor Arena was much larger then than today. The magnificent mock castles and the surrounding woods produced vivid tableaux with a large part of the Aldershot Command involved in the various performances. The massed bands were very impressive but the essential battles, with hundreds of troops kitted accurately in period uniforms, left a lasting impression that no show since has matched even remotely. The Battle of Detingen (1743) was terrific as was the Battle of Waterloo. One year the East Yorks played a major role in the Spanish Armada with Sergeant Kelly taking the part of Drake. Mrs Kelly was of French origin and we were packed off to her quarter on occasion to learn the rudiments of her native tongue, but my brother Ivor and I found her pet parrot too much of a distraction to take our language lessons very seriously. Queen Elizabeth was played by an officer of the Royal Army Service Corps (RASC). The sea battle was imaginatively depicted by a floodlit tableau. The ships were about ¼ mile away near the Basingstoke canal on rails. In the darkness they seemed very real but were actually made of wood and canvas. A World War I scene was made realistic when a replica of the Ypres Cloth Hall was shelled and burnt. An aircraft flew over, probably a Virginia, and electric lamps were lit on it to imitate a hit by anti-aircraft guns with a subsequent fire. Recent Civil Aviation Authority legislation has permitted the towing of advertisements on drogues by aircraft but it was the norm in the early thirties. As the crowds gathered for the Tattoo on fine June evenings before darkness fell, Avro 504N biplanes could be seen towing advertisements over the Arena proclaiming 'Bile Beans Keep You Fit'.

The Long Valley, then as now a military vehicle training area, became a bus park during Tattoo week. The sight of so many vehicles was cause for excitement in those days.

So far as we were concerned at Mandora Lodge, the Tattoo had another value. Our father, the Quartermaster, let us play soldiers with dummy pikes, swords and other paraphernalia until it was time for them to be returned to the makers with the period uniforms.

My association with other officers' children at Miss Seed's School led to an interesting insight into the somewhat unfortunate attitudes struck by some wives in those prewar forces. My father had helped Miss Seed to get the school started around 1928 where I palled up with a young friend, Jack (Langtry). He invited me to tea, obviously without his parent's knowledge. I was not to know this and duly advised my parents of the invitation. On the great day I was cleaned up and the batman was instructed to take me the mile or so to Jack's house. The quarter was similar to ours and on ringing the doorbell, their batman answered the door but seemed unaware of any invitation. He told us to wait while he made enquiries. He returned and said that the lady of the house knew nothing of the invitation and had enquired "what's his father?" On being given Dad's rank and regiment, the host batman returned saying "he can come in." Apparently my host's father was the same rank as mine!

After manoeuvres and annual camp in the late summer, the tents needed drying before storage. A large marquee would miraculously appear on our back garden lawn for a week or two and it made a fine playground. My Auntie Lal had married an NCO in the regiment and our cousin Stanley came to play in the tent. A hot summer's afternoon saw him try the effect of a large tent mallet on Ivor's head. Perhaps it was a release of emotion that prompted the youngsters to try and test the strength of a friend's cranium.

The 1929 Schneider Trophy was won by Great Britain for the second time in succession. It was to be won outright in 1931 when the Supermarine S6B, the forerunner of the Spitfire took the race by being the only serviceable competitor. The 1929 affair was broadcast and I listened to the noise of the engines of each aircraft flying over the Solent by standing on my bicycle and leaning against the open window of the Sergeants Mess where they had a radio (wireless). I was privileged to meet one of those Schneider Trophy pilots years later when Group Captain Snaith became O.C. Flying at Farnborough where I was a Mess Member.

It was a fine morning some time in 1930 when the massive shape of the airship R100 flew over Aldershot coming from the Farnborough direction. It was seemingly quite low. During that summer Uncle Jim invited us as a family to join him on the hill overlooking Hendon aerodrome to view the annual RAF Air Pageant. Hundreds of others watched from this free vantage point. The R101 flew over the show, such a short time before the tragic loss in France a few weeks later. Parachutists dropped from a formation of Vickers Vimys, a standard training practice. The aircraft took off with the trainees standing on small platforms behind the rear outer struts on the wings. They clutched the strut, then at an appropriate time pulled the rip chord allowing the parachute to inflate, dragging each man off the aircraft. An exciting event was the mock attack on a tethered observation balloon which was set on fire after the dummy crew had descended by parachute from the basket. The whole envelope would flare then gather into a ball of flaming fabric which plummeted onto the airfield. Danger to the crowd did not seem to worry anyone nor the expense of destroying a perfectly good balloon. Still, the show was for one day only but I saw the event repeated in 1936 for the last time.

A reduction in the military budget by Parliament in The Geddes Act at the time had reduced our peacetime forces to a bare minimum in the late twenties and early thirties. However, as far as men were concerned they seemed to be plentiful. The battalion strength was swollen by Durham miners who could not get work in the big depression. Regular meals and a good life attracted many to the colours despite low pay and hard discipline. There were over 800 men in the Second Battalion when Drafts would be sent to the First Battalion in India to reinforce the wider Empire defences as overseas troops completed their engagements. Equipment was another matter. It was sad to see troops going out on exercise riding bicycles with silhouettes of Word War I Mother Tanks made of plywood attached to the frames. They represented tanks while on occasion a man with a flag represented a platoon.

From my bedroom in Mandora Lodge we could see the guardroom. A sentry was on duty with rifle, bayonet fixed and with web equipment. He marched up and down or stood at ease according to a fixed timetable. The bugler would blow defaulters every half hour when all men confined to barracks had to run to the guardroom, fall in, and answer their names. Sometimes just two or three were involved but I recall some thirty or so occasionally. Bugle calls were imprinted on our childhood memories, even some of the words handed down from times past. Some do not bear printing but the defaulters call was not profane, it went "You can be on defaulters as long as you like so long as your answer your name."

On a dank misty October day looking out of the window towards the guardroom, I saw the sentry halt at the slope, turn to his front obviously awaiting the passage in front of him of an officer. Sure enough, my Godfather, Major E.B. Robinson, M.C. , a major commanding 'A' Company, rode past on his charger. The sentry gave him a smart butt salute.

The horse was reined to a stop then backed up to the rigid frame of the guard. I could not hear any words but they obviously were flying. With gesticulations it was obvious that the hapless soldier had not noticed that a major was passing and he required a present arms, not a butt salute. The lad was made to present arms a couple of times while being lectured on the error of his ways. This must have been tiresome for the horse who decided that it was a good time to relieve himself. Streams of hot liquid fell on the road creating clouds of steam which enveloped the sentry and his rider. A lasting picture was the bayonet and still gesticulating officer sticking up out of the cloud.

Each 15 June that same officer would ring on our front door bell and give the batman half a crown as a birthday present to his Godson. He became the champion revolver shot in the British Army.

The Battalion had a major success at the Command Small Arms Meeting on Ash Ranges in 1930 sweeping all before them. They won all the trophies except a couple which went to Guards Regiments. My father did particularly well. Dad was not an enthusiastic athlete, although he had been a gymnastic instructor I believe. The falling plate competition required each team to run a few hundred yards then fire at metal plates several hundred yards away. The good runners would be off like hares and then bang away with rifle, heaving as they panted. Dad would amble up behind, lie down and left handed knock the plates down while the rest of the team just stirred up the dust.

My father was an excellent rapid-fire expert but the short Lee-Enfield rifle required a difficult contortion to operate the bolt left-handed. His thumb would get skinned on the joint by a screw head below the bolt. His practice was to take the screw out and replace it by a matchstick to avoid the problem! He had received his commission at St James Palace from King George V and it was a moment fit to make us burst with pride when we all stood beside him in his best uniform on Steeles Road and he saluted the King, with a royal acknowledgement, as the Monarch drove to open the new Vocational Training Centre just east of our barracks.

It was rumoured that Robby usually let a man off a charge for a misdemeanour if he had never heard the excuse before. The bugle blew lights out at 22.15 hrs. All those on late pass had to report to the guardroom by 23.59 hrs usually in uniform and get to bed in the dark. A defaulter was marched into the Orderly Room in front of Robby who asked why had the soldier reported in after 23.59 hours? "Well Sir" he said "I was running for the late train at Waterloo Station after an evening in London and the programme of relayed music at the station between train time announcements was ending so they played the National Anthem. Being in uniform I stood to attention and the train went out before I could catch it", Robby let him off, the batman told me he didn't even check if the Southern Railway did play the National Anthem.

2ᴺᴰ Bɴ. ᴇᴀꜱᴛ Yᴏʀᴋꜱʜɪʀᴇ ʀᴇɢɪᴍᴇɴᴛ
Mᴀɴᴅᴏʀᴀ Bᴀʀʀᴀᴄᴋꜱ Aʟᴅᴇʀꜱʜᴏᴛ
Gᴜᴀʀᴅ Cʜᴀɴɢᴇ ᴀᴜɢᴜꜱᴛ 1927

F. S. Sᴛʀɪɴɢᴇʀ

iv - 2nd Bn. East Yorkshire Regiment, Mandora Barracks, Aldershot. Guard Change, August 1927.

In October 1930 the whole Battalion moved to Catterick Camp in North Yorkshire where they were to be stationed in Menin Lines for the next four years, the normal stint for the infantry at that time. We all moved together in the long trains spaced at intervals on the same day from the Garrison siding at Aldershot. Each officer's family had a first class compartment and the journey to Richmond station took all day. It caused us much amusement at mealtimes when we would stop at a station such as York, a bugler would blow cookhouse on the platform, much to the amazement of civilian travellers, and packed meals would be brought to us. My father had gone ahead a week or so early with the advance party but had made all of the main battalion travel and supply arrangements beforehand.

The surrounding Catterick Camp countryside could not be seen until the next day as we had arrived in the dark. It was so different from Aldershot. Firstly we were nowhere near the barracks, the Battalion had gone into Menin Lines. We were in a large estate of officers' quarters, ours being No. 2 Haig Road. This was different from Aldershot where only the Commanding Officer (CO) and the Quarter Master (QM) had officers' quarters. Catterick offered a sizeable semidetached house to all married officers, certainly above Captain rank. The houses were larger for majors and colonels had large detached residences in Richmond Road. Each wooden front garden gate was emblazoned with a nameplate, usually in wood and painted by the appropriate regimental pioneer sergeant or one of his carpenters. The board indicated the rank, name and regiment (with Battalion) of the resident officer. Ours was lettered in blue and yellow. Many of the resident wives were charming but some seemed to regard the titles as applying to themselves, as if achieved by their own efforts.

We were amazed on the first morning to see that the view from our breakfast table was a field containing a large flock of sheep being gathered by a shepherd and his dog. Nearby were woods and miles of open countryside which became a perfect playground for the many youngsters of our age, all with an army background and mostly attending the same school. Education now became a matter of some serious thought and at the tender age of 8 was promptly enrolled as the youngest member of Richmond Grammar School where I was to learn something of the more rigid discipline extended to my regimental elders.

Chapter 2

SCHOOLDAYS

To me Richmond Grammar School had the shock of a cold shower. For the first year I was bewildered and frightened stiff half of the time. I was in Form I and learned practically nothing except to stand up to bullying, insults and to learn that as a little boy, rugger could be a misery when everyone else was twice your size or seemed so, and you didn't know the rules anyway. Cricket was a bit better. I was a day boarder, kitted out in standard grey suit with stiff white collar. Boarders wore theirs outside the jacket, we wore ours inside. Attention to masters in class was essential otherwise a hard clip around the ear or even a punch in the ribs would result.

The school had been founded in Queen Elizabeth I's reign. Lessons were taken in a monastery looking building near the river Swale, the bridge leading to the railway station (now gone) and the road to Catterick Camp. We travelled by United Bus Company on season tickets. Half fare return was 4d (about 1½p). The boarders lived at the Friary on the other side of Richmond where we had lunch and played organised games. An occasional junior chore was to ring the bell for lunch. It hung outside the dining hall from a bracket on the wall in a wide passage. When cook emerged and nodded, the lad would ring once as a 5 minute warning. When she appeared again, it was the signal for two rings which would result in a hundred or so boys appearing from everywhere to line both sides of the corridor prior to being filed into the meal.

Only once was I picked for the bell ringing job and it was a disaster. I was very nervous and anxious to put up a good show. As I waited, looking at the chord hanging from the clapper, I grew more apprehensive. The cook appeared, by this time I was shaking, she nodded and I grabbed the string, hit the bell but with shaking it rebounded ands truck the other side. Two rings! Out poured the schoolboys from everywhere. In panic I ran down between the ranks shouting, "no not yet, go back", I suppose nowadays I wouldn't give a damn.

It was obvious that I was really too young for the school in 1930-31 but after a second year I began to get the hang of things and eventually came overall sixth in the form. Wise councils decided that I was still too young for the second form so I was held back yet another year. At the end of that one I came top and duly proceeded to Form II aged 11.

Discipline extended everywhere, not just in the classroom. I was caned twice, once for scrambling for a sweet on the floor of the bus and once for tossing pebbles into the goldfish pond in the park.

Lessons extended to the mysteries of Latin, Algebra, Geometry and French. At weekends we had to wear very dark grey suits with pinstripe trousers and our stiff collars. Some of the old spark remained when, dressed in this outfit one Sunday morning, I approached a building site where more quarters were being built in the field opposite our house. Several friends were with me and we saw a metal barrow, a standpipe and tap, and alongside a deep hole half full of water. The temptation to fill the barrow with water then tip the water into the hole was greater than prudence should have suggested. I turned the tap on full and the top flew off. A jet of water hit me in the chest knocking me into the hole. What had been an immaculate Grammar School boy emerged soaked and covered in mud. To make matters worse the standpipe was shooting water many feet into the air. My parent's patience was tested, my mother sorting me out and my father sorting out the building site problem.

Nine of us rode bikes and were able to form a three flight squadron with cigarette cards jammed into the brake block to simulate engine noise. We performed squadron formation manoeuvres on the nearby playing field much to the anger of the army groundsman. Biggles stories in the Modern Boy weekly paper triggered these antics. By sitting the juniors on the handlebars as gunners, we could simulate the World War I FE2bs and have dogfights. The bicycle was a prize possession. Although a Hercules (without 3 speed) cost £3.19.6d the sum of nearly £4 was princely indeed, a working class family having to exist on 30 shillings a week in some instances. The nearby woods were a special attraction since they contained a stream and conifer plantation in addition to deciduous trees. We built huts and dams to catch newts and tadpoles, to the annoyance of a local farmer. It was a moving experience thirty years later to take our daughter, Carol, aged 10 to the same tree where we kids jumped the stream, and she jumped it too.

We would cycle up to the Yorkshire moors to Bellerby Camp to see the Vickers Mk IV tanks and Carden Lloyd Whippets of the 4th Battalion Royal Tank Corps who had the barracks alongside ours at Catterick. The hard slog uphill was well worth the long freewheel at high speed for several miles home.

The co-operation of adults in our fun was nearly always present. We would wait on either side of the Menin Lines end of Haig Road for the large mail van. With toy pistols we would stage a mock hold-up and the postman would lean out of the cab firing a pistol formed by his fingers and thumb making a getaway at high speed from his schoolboy ambush.

A serious interest in aircraft followed my earlier enthusiasms. This was triggered not only by literature I read, but also by the appearance of Skybird Models designed as wooden kits of $^1/_{72}$nd scale by A.J. Holliday. They were very expensive for the time but I believe they put many a young lad onto the road to a career in aviation. Frog and Warnford flying models also gave great enjoyment. We could only afford the cheaper versions, but the more expensive Frog Scale Hart and Puss Moth with a high speed mechanism for winding up the elastic to drive the propeller were of excellent design.

The most important contribution to our aviation interest during those years must certainly be attributed to the Alan Cobham displays. He arrived at Richmond with his fleet of very exciting aircraft to fly from a large field at the side of the main road to Darlington, somewhere near the present site of the mixed comprehensive school which eventually absorbed the Grammar School. Aircraft included the Handley Page W8B and Airspeed Ferry for 10/- and 7/6d joyrides, Avro 504Ns for the five bob flips and Avro Cadets for formation flying. All were biplanes. Crazy flying and glider aerobatics were demonstrated but I was always intrigued by the sight of Geoffrey Tyson flying one of the early Tiger Moths and picking up a handkerchief spread over a small frame on the grass with the aid of a spike on his wingtip. It was with some sense of nostalgia that, on checking my logbook, I discovered that I had flown the same Tiger solo 25 years later.

Snowfalls could be very heavy in winter, making the camp pretty bleak spot. Snowdrifts could make it difficult even to getting food to the chicken run. The army had an answer for everything. One night with a lot of snow on the ground, a large draft bound for the 1st Battalion in Razmac, India, I believe, marched or rather wandered behind the band on their way to Richmond Station. The troops had been given a somewhat alcoholic send off from Menin Lines and any semblance of keeping in step with the band or even in recognisable ranks was non existent. With full kit there was nowhere to carry their Wolsey sun helmets, so they wore them on their heads. The sight of a hundred or so soldiers wearing sun helmets on a dark night in the snow has left an indelible impression.

We had marvellous birthday parties. My June birthday was a help since most of the afternoon and evening was spent outdoors with some 15 or so youngsters let loose. A legendary person was 'Banger' King, a young subaltern who would take a crowd of us on a picnic using his Bentley-like open tourer as a transport. He would stop outside the houses of East Yorks youngsters and ring a milkbell to call us out. Tragically he was killed in Normandy ten years later when his Bren carrier ran over a mine.

To everyone's surprise, the 2nd Battalion had the very unusual experience of a posting back to Aldershot. This time to North Camp, in Malplaquet Barracks, Marlborough Lines. Bandmaster, Fred Harris, was said to have thrown his hat in the air at the news. He transferred to the Guards Brigade later in his career and by strange coincidence, conducted the Guards String Orchestra as the Earl of Athlone presented me, and others, with our degrees in the Albert Hall in 1953 with my father looking on. We met Fred afterwards in a dressing room while he changed into mufti, he had been in Guards uniform on the stage, we met him in long underpants.

The train journey was much as in 1930, but in the opposite direction. This time we had our two canaries, their cages hanging from the roof racks.

We approached our destination along the main line through Woking having circumvented London. We passed the Brooklands racetrack and we were delighted to see a motorbike overtake the train on the railway straight. It was dark when we got to Malplaquet Lodge which was immaculate having been occupied by a Scottish Regiment QM, the Argyll and Sutherland, I believe. The barracks was some 200 yards away. Saturday morning saw Ivor and I on our way to find Farnborough Aerodrome. We walked through South Farnborough then off the main road down a slope to be confronted with our dream world of the wide variety of Royal Aircraft Establishment (RAE) aircraft on the apron on the north side of the field with Hawker Audax army cooperation types of No. 4 Squadron in the north east corner by the RAE South Gate. We found that the whole length of the southern boundary of the airfield was open to us. That first sighting was to be repeated time and again as we spent most of our free days there. As time went on we grew bolder and crept slowly up both east and west boundaries sometimes dangerously close to aircraft. We would edge our way up Jersey Brow towards the catapult when the Blackburn Baffin was to be launched getting almost under the wings. An Air Ministry policeman with a hook hand would appear from his hut at the west end of A shed and rush towards us swinging a broom around his head. We would scatter but then edge back again. Other aircraft on the tarmac were special to the Royal Aircraft Establishment being experimental, others were service types, aircraft that come readily to mind are the Blackburn Twin Engined Monoplane, Gloster Survey, Northrop 2E, a complete variety of Hawker Hart variants, including one with a Dagger engine, Parnell Parasole, Airspeed Courier, Bristol Bulldogs, Gloster Gauntlet prototype, Monospar, Hawker Horsley with Condor engine, Vickers Virginia, Handley Page Heyford, heavy bombers, Westland Wapiti and Wallace, Vickers Vildebeest, Hawker Fury, Gordon, Seal and Heinkel HE70A. Vespa, Shark, Miles Falcon, DH88 Comet (in silver livery with RAF markings) and Queen Bees. It was great to get a wave from the pilot; I wave to youngsters on airfields when I fly myself these days, I hope they get a kick out of it, I did as I entered my teens..

The Bristol 138 gained the world's highest altitude record piloted first by F/Lt Swain and then by F/Lt Adams. The aircraft was very quiet in flight and I was surprised one day to see it quietly gliding low over our house to a landing on the airfield.

It is something of a coincidence that the Comet should return to Farnborough half a century later to be rebuilt by RAE apprentices to flying condition. It must have delighted many visitors to Farnborough Air International 1984 to see this beautiful aircraft resplendent in its original red livery on static display in F1 hangar.

In January 1993 I witnessed the demolition of the last of four very large sheds on the old RAE site, until early in 1993 one was used as a surplus furniture store. My father worked in the building for a short time after World War II. It had been part of the Army land between the

v - Vickers Vespa and an RAE starter vehicle, circa 1934.

World Wars. The space between these buildings, which had been constructed during the first World War as part of the Royal Aircraft Factory
– probably for aircraft production, was occupied by a long row of many
surplus or reserve World War I tanks. They remained there for many
years, I remember them well. But in about 1935 they were cut up for
scrap. Many children, including us, collected large ball bearings from the
gun turrets and elsewhere. I have never seen a photograph of the tanks,
but the four corrugated iron sheds can be seen in many existing airborne
photographs. By World War II the buildings were still within the bounds
of Elles Barracks (Royal Tank Corps, and then the RASC). After the war
they were included within the RAE boundary. Three were demolished
well before the destruction of the last one on the south western part of
the total area included by the original four buildings.

No.4 Squadron occupied what were later known during Society of
British Aircraft Constructors (SBAC) shows as the 'Black Sheds'. One
remains, it became RAE Fire Station for a while. We would move along
the dirt road between the RAF Officers Mess and the airfield, near where
Cody made his first flight, and up to the Hawker Andax or sometimes a
Cierva C32 Rota autogiro. Visiting aircraft offered further variety and I
learned a lesson in life from one of them. A Vickers Valentia troop carrier

was parked pointing north at the end of the tarmac. We slowly moved forward until under the shadow of its starboard wing and stayed there all morning. As lunchtime approached an airman set off to walk to the barracks half a mile behind us. On the spur of the moment, I said, "Is it alright if we stay here?" "No", he said "B – off". Which just goes to show.

The airfield was about a quarter of its present size, Laffans Plain was still a grass area but not used for flying. We used to fly our 'Scud' glider and elastic driven models there – where Cody once flew his 'Cathedral'. We went to school with Samuel Cody's grandson and he followed his father and grandfather into the fabric shop at the RAE. He showed us two crosses on the ground which marked the spot where the aviation pioneer Colonel Cody and his passenger were killed near a row of oak trees. The crosses disappeared during the World War II development of Y20 building in the area. Three trees that Cody hit are still there, but the crosses are nowhere to be seen.

The astounding performance of the pre 1939 aircraft in terms of take off and landing was illustrated by two Virginias I saw with gunners in the open rear cockpits, take-off in formation from the site of the old Flying Control Building (N1) and then clear the hill which these days accommodates the SBAC static show, a matter of some 500 yards.

At the end of each working day around 5.30 pm or 12.30 on Saturdays, streams of cyclists could be seen riding along the road to the RAE South Gate. That was a signal for us to cross the grass field which then claimed its status as common land and we rushed to the hangars to look at the aircraft through the gaps between the doors in A Shed. We could smell a dope and petrol mixture which spelt real aeroplanes to us. I saw a Heyford night bomber have brake failure near Jersey Brow and collide with the open 'A' Shed door, shutting the sliding heavy structure with the impact. We both had a very narrow squeak when the Northrop 2E nearly landed on top of us. This aircraft was a tandem two seat low wing monoplane of advanced design for the period. It sported a pair of large fairings or pants over each undercarriage leg. This powerful aircraft was probably being piloted by Flying Officer Clouston on this occasion; it was one of a number of American aircraft evaluated by the Air Ministry from time to time. Another to appear at Farnborough was a tricycle undercarriage cabin biplane, the Waco D coloured bright red. However, returning to the Northrop, it was obviously very difficult to land on such a small field as Farnborough and the pilot on this occasion made a very flat approach aiming to make maximum use of every bit of the ground between the south-east and north-west corners of the airfield. He approached on a heading of about 330° flared as the slope dropped away on the approach and actually touched down about 25 yards inside the airfield boundary, missing Ivor and me by what seemed to be inches as we ran ducking down the path which is now the south perimeter road.

vi - Heinkel He70A in the RAE 24ft Wind Tunnel, circa 1936. (RAE)

Clouston was a very brave and extremely capable pilot, he was well known for his long distance flying and later for his daring attempts to cut balloon cables with wing leading edge devices designed by RAE.

Our leisure reading matter had now spread to Popular Flying at 6d a month, Air Stories at 7d a month and eventually the Aeroplane at 6d a week, the latter being paid for by my father because he enjoyed the leading articles by the editor, C.G. Gray. Ivor and I joined the Aldershot County High School, subsequently attended by our daughter, Carol. The change from the strict discipline of Richmond was very acceptable though it did not necessarily improve my academic progress. One reason for this was that the High School was coeducational. Having girls in the class was very strange to me. I spent a lot of time just looking at them. It seemed they had the best facilities, including the use of the adjacent sports field, ours was half a mile away, and I was not used to lady teachers anyway. The girls seemed to do better than the boys in most subjects. I joined the cadet force but it was limited in scope. We drilled once a week and spent quite a lot of time forming fours and marching up and down. There were no uniforms. The C.O. was our history master, Brindley Thomas, an ex major with wartime service in the Royal Artillery. The masters were a cheerful lot on the whole, Archie Maunders taught Chemistry and allowed us to make advanced things like fireworks, Smiler Miles taught French, Doc Naish – English and Latin and Nobby Clarke, Maths. Nobby was one of the old school of teachers, he could control a class with just a word and his lessons can be recalled 57 years later. The headmaster was Mr Chapman who was respected and loved by all of the students and teachers alike. He took holy orders on his retirement from Farnborough Grammar School just before the war. Dickie Richards taught us Geography and was a first class teacher who laid the foundations of my interest in navigation and map reading. Doc Naish was our form master in 1935 and was well known for liking a pint or two in the evenings. He also taught us Religious Knowledge or Scripture as it was termed. He found biblical condolence for his liking for a drop of beer by quoting the text "and St Paul took courage". I do not recall the bible spells courage with a capital C.

A few of us rode through Elles Barracks on the north side of RAE one afternoon. It was the home of the 2nd Battalion Royal Tank Corps. Some long sheds which had at one time been part of the old Royal Aircraft Factory during World War I had become the resting place of a hundred or so of the tanks mentioned earlier. Two RAE outbuildings on the edge of the Royal Tanks playing field were G1 and ˙G2 where I was to work for a few years during and after the war. On the afternoon in question we were staggered to see the engineless airframe of a Bristol Fighter, obviously discarded at the side of G2 near the boiler house. We were examining it carefully when a man in overalls appeared to ask what we were doing. We asked him why the aircraft was there and he said it was scrapped. Could we take some bits? He did not see why not, we spent a couple of days more or less dismantling it. Taking struts and flare brackets etc home. On the second day an RAE policeman appeared and took our names. We dashed home to tell our fathers and mine went to see the inspector. We were allowed to keep the bits but apparently the man who gave us permission to take them was not an authorised personage, he was the boiler man!

In September 1936 the school split. The girls stayed in Aldershot and the boys went to the new building in Prospect Avenue, Farnborough, now the Sixth Form College. We were joined by the boys of the Farnborough Secondary School to become the Farnborough Grammar School under the headship of Arthur Chapman. The 360 odd boys did not mix readily and rivalry between the Aldershot and Farnborough factions resulted in frequent fights. Mr Chapman gradually settled us down and a fine spirit of unity had emerged by 1937 when the school won the trophy at the county sports at Winchester. I was the reserve junior high jump man that day having won the school junior record in our own sports day earlier in the year. It was a good job that a tall lad called Pollicut jumped instead of me. He did far better than I know I was able to do and we scraped home by the points margin provided by his efforts in winning his event at Winchester.

I recall a school outing to the British Industries Fair. A large contingent of boys went to Waterloo by rail from Farnborough. One of our number was Dickie Moor. I believe his father was in the Indian Army and Dickie

vii - Drawing by Mr Foster, the Art Master at Farnborough Grammar School, 1939.

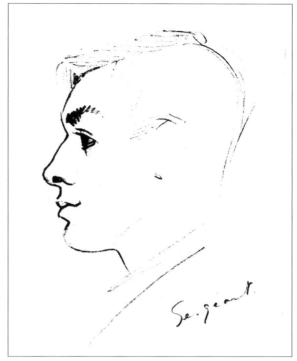

himself went on to do great things during World War II. He proved his spirit of courage and skill, though in a somewhat foolhardy manner by accepting a dare. As the train sped between Clapham Junction and Waterloo, probably the busiest line in the world, he opened the compartment door next to mine and entered ours having edged along the carriage outside running board. He epitomised a spirit typical of many of those boys, several of whom were to die in combat a short while later.

Work now became a serious business as the School Certificate grew near. I took the exam during that memorable summer when Len Hutton scored his fantastic record score against the Australians in the test match. Having achieved the essential qualification early it was necessary to obtain the more coveted Matriculation which offered an entrance to University. The Grammar and Secondary schools were fee paying, although some scholarship boys places were free. A means test decided if a scholarship would be granted. My father's salary exceeded the limit apparently so he had to pay for his two boys. It was about 5 guineas each a term which meant a significant contribution at the time, books uniforms, fares and all supporting items having to be paid for in addition. We travelled to and from Marlborough Lines – school buses, three Aldershot & District double deckers were hired for the Aldershot and Farnborough journey to accommodate pupils of the old High School. It was all great fun. We would sing, particularly "An apple for the teacher" and other hits of the day.

Another year in Form VC provided me with Matric and top position in the form in what was a very happy association with some wonderful lads. Nearly all did either very well in one profession or another in later life as was the norm for the school. Sadly several in the various fifth and sixth forms were killed during the war which was looming.

15 September 1936 was memorable in two ways. Firstly the Grammar School was opened and secondly the 2nd East Yorks sailed for Palestine leaving the families and a cadre behind in Aldershot mostly in Napier and Grant Square, recently demolished. The troubles in Palestine, a British Protectorate required reinforcements and my father sailed in the troopship, Nevassa with the Battalion. He found it a very active period but returned in late 1937 to transfer the families to Crownhill Barracks, Plymouth prior to the return of the regiment. Their place was taken in Aldershot by the Leicester Regiment and our old friends, the Wale family from Catterick, moved into Malplaquet Lodge. My brother went to Plymouth too but so as not to upset schooling, I was lodged with the Bale family for a while in Oudenarde Lodge. Subsequently arrangements were made through my headmaster for me to move into digs in Highgate Lane, Farnborough with Mr & Mrs Martin. He was an Aldershot & District bus driver on the run to London. It was in these circumstances that I had a birthday party and one of the neighbouring girls invited was Renée Porter, who some eight years later became my wife.

Mrs Martin introduced me to Farnborough Old Parish Church where I attended evening service. The Church was to become part of my life. We were married there, Carol was christened and confirmed there and both Renée's and my parents were buried from there. Renée had also been confirmed there in those days of Canon Challacombe, the Rector. Years later I was to become deputy Churchwarden and Churchwarden covering some 25 years before being awarded the honour of Churchwarden Emeritus. Renée who died on 19 May 1995 was buried in Ship Lane after a sad and memorable service by Canon Alan Bodington in the church.

Ivor didn't settle in Plymouth and he was re-entered at Farnborough Grammar School and we both moved into digs with the Hildred family in Chingford Avenue, Bob Hildred was a schoolfriend who joined the RAF during the war to become a pilot in Coastal Command. He was killed during an attack on a German U Boat as described later.

In 1939 there was a silver frost one Sunday morning, Ivor and I tried to walk to the 8am Holy Communion at church but had to give up, the ground was so slippery. Everything was glazed ice; we could not stand up without support and failed to get over the railway bridge footpath along the 'Mounts' walk, a path that was to shape much of my future.

I persuaded Brindley Thomas one damp afternoon while supporting a school soccer match that something should be done to enliven the School Cadet Force. He listened to my arguments and suggestions. It was a bit of a cheek since I was only a 16 year old pupil. Nevertheless to my surprise He said "Yes, go ahead, I will support you." He let me form two companies, the senior one in resurrected uniforms, all with puttees. With drill type rifles and old cavalry carbines we managed to provide most of the cadets with the means of some tactical work in addition to drill. Another surprise was that the Headmaster agreed to my suggestion that all of Friday afternoon should be devoted to Cadets. It was great fun. After some time as a Cadet Sergeant I emerged as the RSM, starting lectures on a variety of subjects which were regarded as acceptable as the war situation grew more serious.

We had an annual inspection when a general from somewhere or another inspected us at a parade followed by various demonstrations. It was during one march past that one hapless chap's puttee started to unwind as he approached the saluting base. He marched past smartly with several feet of khaki cloth trailing behind him. Later he became a Brigadier.

I recall that I introduced defaulters. Any lad who did not behave was given extra drill, it didn't make me very popular but it smartened the platoons up. Some spectators were amused on one occasion to see their colleagues marching up and down on the small playground, their derisory laughter was quelled when they had to fall in with the others. I do not seem to have been forgiven for some of my Army Cadet endeavours. Several Cadets later joined RAE and one or two, in their late fifties, were quick to remind me of my attempts forty years earlier to persuade them to act and look regimental!

I took matriculation during 1939. That school year in Form VB was probably the happiest of my schooldays. Coming first overall academically in the form and working among close friends was fun. I was keen on cricket and as a bowler was in the school first XI for a while.

That fateful year saw a gradually worsening international situation. The Munich crisis had given us a taste of things to come when some of us volunteered to dig trenches for air raid protection in North Camp under floodlights. As we broke up for our summer holiday we went home this time to 15 Orchard Road where my mother had taken a rented house, my father, by this time, had been transferred from the East Yorks to the Royal Ordnance Corps as an attachment. He was responsible for the provision, maintenance and support for all anti-aircraft defence in the West Yorkshire area from Sheffield to Leeds. His headquarters was at Robertown near Huddersfield where he had the largest of his several depots. As the war drew near he advised my mother that he would prefer us, with him, so we packed up at Orchard Road and travelled north. The train was lit by blue electric lights producing a dramatic effect, since we had no idea what would happen if war was declared, which indeed it was, just one week later on 3rd September 1939.

We arrived at the 'Star Inn', Robertown and immediately started to investigate the 3.7 inch anti-aircraft guns and searchlights in the store. The only guard was a watchman! Boredom set in, very quickly relieved only by the excitement of the air raid alarm on the Sunday morning that war was declared and another that night. We all gathered on the stairs clutching our gas masks in their cardboard boxes in the dark; and nothing happened on either occasion. We wandered outside before the all clear to find most of the menfolk in the village had done the same. Memories of the 'Star' include unreasonably large helpings of Yorkshire Pudding and crown bowls on the green at the rear of the pub. The phoney war had started. We moved a mile or so away to a large house where we lodged with an elderly man and his wife. The boredom became intense. The grounds contained guinea fowl and Ivor and I would while away the time aiming a large cider bottle at them from an upstairs bedroom window hauling the missile back on an attached string, ready for another go.

My father's driver, Jim, nearly wrote the two of them off in a nasty collision while driving between depots. One of the staff cars was a Lanchester with an early form of automatic gearbox. During quiet periods Jim would give me driving lessons around the depot. The advent of war produced a change at the gate. Much to my father's consternation, a platoon of troops, presumably national servicemen, was despatched to look after depot security. Sentries were everywhere and they set up camp in the field next to the depot. Life got exciting since these lads were keen and a bit twitchy. After several innocent civilian inhabitants had been shot at when taking a night time short cut across the fields, father decided that enough was enough. So the troops were withdrawn and the watchman came back!

We were shaken out of any mood of complacency by news of the sinking of the battleship Royal Oak in Scapa Flow and the loss of HMS Courageous. We had made a model of the latter, an aircraft carrier, in previous days. The South Atlantic battle and sinking of the Graf Spee, German pocket battleship, gave us heart however.

It was with great relief that we heard that the Farnborough Grammar School would re-open in November, so Ivor and I returned to Farnborough and were put into digs at the home of Mr and Mrs Hildred. Their only son, Bob, was a schoolfriend. Our relatively long stay of some four months at the Hildred's not was too happy but we got on reasonably well. I was now a prefect in the sixth form taking science and Bob was on the arts side. As mentioned earlier, he joined the RAF later and became a pilot in Coastal Command flying the Fortress I on anti-submarine operations. Sadly he was reported missing from one operation, believed to have been as a result of an attack on a U boat in the Atlantic. Mr Hildred had served in World War I as a signaller in the Lincolnshire Regiment. He delighted in teaching us the Morse Code during that winter using a homemade key and buzzer. Those lessons have stood me in good stead since. Boredom was relieved by visits on Wednesday evenings to the local dance or hop in the Church Hall at Frimley. For two bob we could vie with the Canadian soldiers to persuade girls to dance. The Canadians had the advantage so we resorted to getting a crowd of girls

vii - 1940 Farnborough Grammar School - Cadet Force General's Inspection Parade. RSM F. S. Stringer on the left.

and friends to go as a party to ensure our share of the goods. The winter was severe.

I recall that a sergeant major had been reported killed on the Western Front, probably on patrol. The newspapers said that there would be an enquiry. Five months later things were very different when the real shooting began. There was great excitement when the "wireless" reported some German destroyers had been sunk in a naval action.

In April 1940 Mum came down from Yorkshire and set up home at Malmo, Leopold Avenue, Farnborough. We were only too glad to get into own place, particularly as this newly built four bedroom modern house on land had been part of the Empress Eugenie's estate, her home until the 1930s. Her house now accommodates the Farnborough Hill Convent College. During that year the VI Science form had an interesting diversion for a boys' school. For some reason the girl science students did not have a laboratory at the Convent College on Farnborough Hill. Three girls joined us for laboratory work. As a special mission I was selected to take marked exercise books up to the convent and was rather overawed by the grandeur of the place. One of the girls became an air hostess after the war.

Much time was spent digging air raid shelters including one in the back garden where we spent many nights in the summer of 1940.

The spring was warm and dry when the German Blitz started in Europe. Our large map on the wall beside the radio in the hall at home had pins and white ink lines marking the retreat of the BEF through

35

Belgium and France. I recall the terrible sadness as France fell and our soldiers began to appear dressed only in battledress wearing tin hats but no equipment. The evacuation of Dunkirk triggered the call by Anthony Eden for all able-bodied men to join the Local Defence Volunteers (LDV). As a minor I needed parental permission to join, so a telegram went to Yorkshire with the welcome reply "OK if friends joining also". Tony Lax an old schoolfriend and I duly presented ourselves at a reception centre, got a denim overall uniform, cap and Hampshire Regiment Cap Badge and LDV armband, and we were in! Some nights later we got our weapons but that story can wait until the next chapter.

One August afternoon Ivor and I went to visit an old Richmond Grammar schoolfriend, Peter Hayes, whose uncle had a flat over a shop in North Camp. The sirens went and we looked out of the window to see a formation of aircraft flying at about 1500 feet over RAE travelling east. We thought they were short nose Blenheims until we noticed bombs falling. The aircraft were Junkers 88s! As the explosions shook the building we made a mad scramble downstairs as machine gun bullets sprayed Lynchford Road. Ivor and I vied for the cover of a doormat for protection.

On another occasion, a 'Wings for Victory' show in the Town Hall used some of our model aircraft. The centrepiece was a real Messerschmitt ME 109e, not too badly damaged. We did a watchman duty to save our models from being pinched; unsuccessfully as it emerged since some were missing at the end of the show. On the Saturday lunchtime Ivor was looking after the display and thought that as things were quiet he would climb in the German aircraft cockpit. While sitting there the sirens sounded the alert and a lone enemy aircraft flew over and machine-gunned the locality. He felt extremely silly sitting in the Messerschmitt in such circumstances.

The war situation made serious schoolwork almost impossible. Air raid alarms and occasionally we would be graced by the presence overhead of enemy aircraft. I was nominated spotter and alarm bell man for the school, probably because as head boy I normally rang electric bells for lesson changes. My problem was to make the 400 or so youngsters evacuate the building and run across the playing field to the shelter. They would stop and chat on the way. I was very agitated one day as the usual drift across the field was taking place but on this occasion with a Junkers JU88 at about 3000 feet overhead. The serious air raid on the Vickers factory at Brooklands by Junkers JU87 dive bombers one lunchtime resulted in many of the lads climbing on to the top of the shutters to see if they could catch a glimpse of the aircraft.

We took great pride in bringing our service gas masks and helmets to school as one-upmanship to advertise our membership of the Local Defence Volunteers and later the Home Guard. Walking home one bright afternoon along Farnborough Road with Tony, we witnessed a gigantic dogfight going on at high altitude overhead. Vapour trails were occasionally visible but the aircraft looked like fish flashing in the sun. There was the whine of overspeeding engines and the occasional noise of high speed machine gun fire. The fight was typical of the Battle of Britain. It went on for some time and we managed to put on our tin hats and stand on Tony's air raid shelter to get a good view. I fell off in my excitement, fortunately with only minor injury, plus a bit of dented pride.

Attempts to study for Inter B.Sc became almost impossible amid the excitement of running the cadets, Home Guard duties lasting all night, an exciting girl friend whom I eventually married, together with disturbed nights due to air raids particularly as the autumn 1940 Blitz started on London. Additionally there was the added nagging feeling that being at school was wrong. I should be fighting the war. Boredom was reflected in our gradual acceptance of trips to the shelter down the garden during the night. We were converting the wood, the area in which the home, Malmo, had been built into a garden. This required a lot of digging, so on moonlight nights we would leave the shelter and do some gardening. One always felt braver if doing something rather than sitting and listening to bumps in the night.

One evening early in October 1940 I was guarding the main line railway bridge at Farnborough. It was an early two-hour stint but already it was dark. As I halted at the northeastern end of the pavement (now part of the A325 actual road) Renée Porter and Peter James, friends of mine, still at school, came up and talked to me. I told them to go away since I was on duty. They went some way down Highgate Lane and Peter whispered something to Renée. She then approached me again, clearly armed with Peter's advice. She pressed the button on my rifle to release the bayonet and ran off with it. I shouted at her in vain for some time, threatening I recall, to shoot her. I could not bear to think of the consequences if she didn't bring it back. After some minutes she did return it while I stayed on post. Next day I asked Peter to fix a date for me. We went for a walk on 10 October 1940 in an air raid and on 14 July 1945 married each other.

Renée and I would go for walks in the blackout usually to sit and talk on a park bench along a footpath called the Mounts on the east boundary of the grounds of Farnborough Abbey. We would wait for the seat to be vacant then sit and talk and frequently sing all the latest hits for hours, frozen to the marrow. We would see the sky above London if we turned around to watch the twinkling lights of anti-aircraft gunfire. The night of the great fire raid on London made that sky light up with a dull red glow even though we were 30 miles away.

Clothing was rationed and coupons were essential. Renée saved hers and cadged more from her family to buy a white mohair coat. She gave it a first outing on one of our visits to the Mounts seat, which had acquired a muddy puddle with the continual impact of courting feet. We were chatting quietly when the gradually increasing sound of a falling bomb entered our otherwise engaged minds. As the rushing noise increased, I grabbed Renée and pushed her to the ground, lay on top of her and yelled "put your hands over your ears!" Poor girl! She thought her virginity was in danger. A muffled sound from her wriggly form under me was audible as the bomb sound suddenly stopped and there was no bang. It was a delayed action, or a dud, and we learned later that it was some way off. She got to her feet, furious, her white coat covered in mud. I was marched off to her Mum waiting for us at their front gate in Highgate Lane to explain. A loving future mother-in-law was so pleased to see us in one piece, she didn't even raise an eyebrow at the state of the coat nor questioned how it happened to achieve its sorry state. She thought I had saved Renée's life or would have if the bomb had been near and gone off and couldn't care less about the state of the coat needing sending to the cleaners.

I was interviewed by a Royal Air Force recruiting team to determine my potential as aircrew. That discussion indicated that I might make a pilot or navigator. However my immediate inclination was to attempt a Sandhurst entry for an Army commission. In advance of such a course I pressed for release from school to do some kind of war effort. I was encouraged by my engineering drawing master to go into the Royal Aircraft Establishment as a temporary laboratory assistant and by my Physics master, Mr R.G. Smith, not to. The former won and on 9 June 1941 I went for interview and started work leaving full time education for good. By this time I was all but 19 and believed that the war was the more important. So ended school days.

Chapter 3

HOME GUARD

The Home Guard was nothing like the Dad's Army as portrayed by television in recent years. It was tough for most of us as some of my recollections will show, I trust. We were civilians at work and soldiers for most of the rest of the time. Some of it was fun, much of it was a job done very seriously by something like one million men. A saving grace in terms of 'doing one's bit' was firstly the Local Defence Volunteers (LDV) and then the Home Guard as it became known upon the suggestion of Winston Churchill. Once that initial enlistment had been achieved, the next ambition was to get hold of a weapon. Our opportunity arrived one wet summer evening when a lot of American P14 .300 calibre rifles were issued to us in the Empress Estate wood. They were covered in grease and straw and were laid in the mud. Obviously straight out of the US Army reserve store and of World War I vintage, but in the circumstances more than welcome. I grabbed one lying in the mud, got 15 rounds of ammunition and bore it home proudly to spend hours cleaning it, Tony got one too.

Our headquarters were in Cove and number 2 Platoon B Coy 25 Hants H.G. (Rotherwick) comprised some 150 men, young lads, reserved occupation types and Word War I veterans, all volunteers. Soon after we were formed we all gathered in Blenheim Barracks, Aldershot one Sunday morning to be addressed by our Colonel, Col. Guinness. The 1940 summer situation was desperate and invasion was expected. He told us that our 15 rounds must kill 15 Germans. Such a score has never been achieved in anger to my mind, even by the best professionals, but we believed him.

In the early days I was one of the unlucky lads who had to act as cycle orderly to the Colonel. I would ride out to a house, now a school, on Fern Hill, Blackwater, and stay the night in a small room next to the old stables, sleeping on a wire bed fully dressed in denims, etc. The CO would stick his head in the door to see if all was well during the late evening. He was in uniform but one night he stuck his head in too far and I noticed that he had put his forage cap on but the rest of him was in a dinner jacket with appropriate tie, etc.

We were allotted key points for guard duty and for mustering in the event of invasion. Our platoon looked after the Trunk Road, Cove Road and Prospect Road Railway Bridge under the main Waterloo – Basingstoke railway line. We kept our rifles and kit near our beds just in case. On a Saturday night in mid-summer I awoke to hear the unmistakeable noise of the Parish Church Bells, the invasion warning. My father was at home on leave. I leapt out of bed shouting 'they're coming!' Too inexperienced and excited to dress, I threw my denim overalls over my pyjamas, gathered my kit and headed for the door. My father suggested that I should wait for him while he, like a real soldier, dressed properly in his uniform, loaded his revolver and agreed that we should set off to find Tony, get him up and then I should get on my way to the bridge at Prospect Road. We took a short cut through the woods and bumped into someone in a dark uniform. We could not see him properly in the blackout but he was wearing a helmet. Dad pushed his revolver into the suspect's stomach and said "who are you?" The man stammered, convincing us that he was a suspect. Actually he was an air raid warden who was too scared to speak. We apologised and pressed on. The air raid post still remains in a back garden. Houses were built on the plot after the war.

Having got Tony out and kitted up we set off to war, little realising that the whole episode was a false alarm. We were challenged as we approached the bridge by someone who had beaten us to it. We didn't want a premature end to our war effort so did exactly as we were told. On the invitation to advance and be recognised, we discovered that our challenger hadn't got a rifle or any other weapon! How I regretted not having put on some warm clothing. In later months we had battledress and put denims and a greatcoat over them to keep warm. Also issue Army boots and gaiters. We waited all night for something to happen; there were air raids in the distance, but nothing more. We were released for a meal and clean up next morning but told to remuster at the Old Post Office at 1400hrs. A half explanation of the alert was given to us but rumours were rife. The favourite being that the Germans had tried to land but had been stopped by flaming petrol poured onto the sea. Of course the wireless said nothing, neither did the papers on the Monday morning. Post war narrative revealed that the bells rang that night over much of the country but there are conflicting accounts of what started them off.

We were taught to shoot and were issued with a Lewis gun, a US pattern aircraft version, which Tony christened Mavis. We learned unarmed combat and started to enjoy ourselves. I was made a corporal and given a squad. We had two sergeants, my art master, Mr Foster, and our Classics master, Jimmy James. How different they seemed in a new environment. Sgt. Foster told us some naughty stories that staggered us, being still at school ourselves. He treated us as men! We did a 1940 guard duty at Starve Acre, a large fir copse overlooking the Farnborough/Aldershot area as far as Guildford. We had a tree house as a look out with plotter to register bomb bursts or parachute landings and a hut at the foot of the tree with bunks. The squad of six or eight would be taken out from Farnborough by an RASC driver in a 15 cwt truck and brought back at 0630 next morning to go back to school or work as the case might be.

We had a heath fire one evening. No amount of beating the brushwood would put it out completely. It crept along under the bracken and would spring up again. Apart from drinking water, we had no other means of

ix - No.607 Squadron defending Sunderland, 15th August 1940. F.S.S. painting for Flight Lieutenant W. E. Blackadder and the other pilots in the action.

damping it down at Starve Acre. Sgt. Foster therefore ordered us all to relieve ourselves on anywhere smoke appeared. It was a gradually decreasing performance as each man dried up in turn.

Excitement one night was occasioned when Ivor was one of the guard. Someone put paraffin in the kettle then lit the primus stove in the hut! They survived after pandemonium as the whole affair filled the hut with flames.

As I watch I can see the same copse and tree some 3 miles to the north on the skyline from Beverley Fair, our present house. We were on guard on the evening of 15 September 1940; Jimmy James brought news to us that the RAF had shot down some 360 odd German aircraft that day. (The Battle of Britain History by R.T. Bickers states that the BBC announced the losses as 183). The figure was subsequently revised to 59 or so. Nevertheless it was a turning point in the Battle of Britain and we were all delighted. Naturally the battle was not known by that name then, but we knew that it was decisive for our survival as a nation.

One summer evening I was telephoned by Lt Instone, our platoon commander and local garage owner and told to gather six men and report for a special all night job. A truck would take us to Hartford

Bridge Flats and we were to guard the site until about 0630 hrs the next day when the army would relieve us. We arrived with 15 rounds each plus rations supplied by the RASC. I was staggered to see that my charge was a new airfield (later known as Blackbushe) complete with three Whitley bombers and an unfurnished control tower! The aircraft were unattended. We did our stuff as efficiently as possible mounting guard over the aircraft with two hours on duty and four off. We slept under issue blankets on the control tower concrete floor. The vast area of runways and taxiways had to look after themselves. Next morning there was no sign of transport. It got to 8.00am and one of the privates got stroppy because he had to go to work. I got enough old buck to put him on a charge. The truck arrived eventually and I believe some action was taken against the lad. I'm not sure what. Serious offences were dealt with by civil courts, a strange arrangement since we appeared to be half soldiers and half civilians.

A regular guard duty was at the Old Post Office where were put on duty at the railway bridge. Marching up and down in pre-war style was accompanied by bags of swank as the critical eyes of beer drinkers around the door of the Station Hotel watched us intently. It was always a mystery to me why we did not look under the bridge. The attraction was the stopping of pedestrians to check their identity cards. It would have been an intensely statistical experiment to count the proportion of girls to the rest of the population who were stopped. It was on one of these guards that my meeting with Renée, the bayonet incident happened.

One night when I was off duty an ATS girl arrived at the guard rooms having walked up from the station in the early hours of the morning with no transport available for her to get to camp. Company Sergeant Major (CSM) Lee was in charge of the guard. He invited her to stay the night, but to ensure no fun and games by the guard placed his 'biscuits', the short issue mattresses and blankets between the girl and the young lads. She departed safely at daybreak.

We did guard duties at the telephone exchange in South Farnborough as well as at the Old Post Office. On separate occasions at each location a man let off a rifle. At the Post Office he was sitting down and the bullet went round the room but injured no one. The telephone exchange incident was more hairy. Sgt. Williams, the Grammar School woodwork master, Welsh and nicknamed Willy-Woodocks, ordered the guard to port arms for inspection outside the exchange. Each rifle magazine was to be charged, that is loaded but the bolt was run over the rounds without 'one up the spout.' The spring was eased by squeezing the trigger and safety catch applied. Willy committed the crime of noting that one lad had not squeezed the trigger. Instead of telling him to check that a live round was not in the breach, then easing the spring, Willy pressed the trigger himself! The rife fired and the bullet missed the other guards but entered the exchange window and buried itself in the telephone board beside an operator.

After a few months No.2 Platoon divided due to its large size and I joined the new No. 4 Platoon commanded by 'Sam' Weller, an ex senior NCO from the Royal Tank Corps. He ran a sweet and tobacconists shop on the Farnborough Road.

In addition to rifles, we were issued with a variety of grenades including the 36 (Mills Bomb), Molotov Cocktails, phosphorous and oil or petrol in a glass bottle, an awkward yellow Thermos size and shape anti-tank bomb with a tape round the top, the no. 73. This latter bomb was a cause of much trouble. The tape was wound round the neck of the container, one end connected to the pin, the other to a small lead weight. This weight would cause the tape to unwind if the bomb was thrown correctly. The pin was withdrawn as the tape was completely unwound. Frequently the thing did not go off. We had a Corporal Tandy, an accountant, I believe, who had been on a course of training on dealing with dud bombs. The normal technique was to blow the dud up with another bomb. On one occasion, a fine Saturday afternoon, we were practicing with live 73 bombs near Minley on the military area used by the Royal Engineers Depot today. One bomb failed to explode. It fell in heather and scrub. The CO thought that another should be lobbed with it. That one didn't go off either. While contemplating the next move, the Salvation Army van appeared with tea and wads, so the men immediately formed a queue and availed themselves of the refreshments. Meanwhile CSM Lee, I believe, decided another 73 might do the trick, it did! All three went up with an enormous wallop, Rumour had it that a window was broken in Blackwater and a cup of tea blown out of a man's hand as he stood by the van.

We received grenade instruction from the Army and we used local ranges in the Aldershot area for both small arms and bomb practice. I had a course of instruction then had to teach others. Practice with live grenades could be exciting. The 36 fuses were either 4 or 7 seconds. We would prime boxes of bombs and get into a trench, which had two escape routes. I found it somewhat unnerving to note a chap's hand shaking as he removed the pin. In his anxiety to get rid of it, the student was apt to forget his drill and lob it incorrectly. This would cause the grenade to hit the parapet and roll back into the trench. Hence the escape routes.

A sergeant from another platoon, a local chemist, looked round the trench corner on one such occasion on hearing a scuffle. The grenade exploded and split his horn-rimmed spectacles in half, but caused him no personal injury. A Canadian Sergeant saved the life of one chap by throwing him out of the trench as a bomb fell back.

We fired 30 type grenades from a cup discharger fitted to a rifle barrel. The rifle butt was supported on the ground with the man sitting or half lying on the ground. The rifle was cocked at an upward angle and a ballastite cartridge inserted in the breech. A 36 grenade fitted with a circular base plate, or a Molotov cocktail was placed in the cup after the safety pin had been withdrawn from the bomb. Aim was crudely achieved by sheer judgement. The trigger was plucked since the cartridge produced an enormous kick. The grenade had the circular plate attached to allow full benefit of the explosive charge. The striker arm came out as the bomb left the cup. A small flat fronted anti-tank grenade was also fired from the cup discharger. It was grey in colour and looked like a small aircraft bomb. We fired at old tanks on Caesars Camp Ranges or the Fox Hills. I hit a tank with one on a Sunday morning and was shaken to receive a very near miss as the tail of the bomb flew back on a reciprocal track and buried itself in the sand at the side of my foot. I kept it for years as a souvenir. Sticky bombs were supplied in large quantities. They were glass spheres with a sticky substance on the outside and a plastic handle with fuse and pin attached. For transit they were enclosed in a clam-like metal cover. We had to approach the tank, smash the glass on it, release the pin and walk calmly away while counting, then lie down a second before the explosion was due. We did some practice in the open. Sergeant Martin, my old landlord was a bomb instructor; he was rather broad in the beam. A lad placed a sticky bomb after smashing it correctly, then Alf Martin shouted 'Down' after walking away. He had just bent down, presenting his expansive rear end to the target and was promptly hit there by a splinter from the Bakelite bomb handle. Again, the bomb was loaded with phosphorous.

Some 35 years after the war, sticky bombs and other explosives were reported as being unearthed as post war development in the Aldershot area spread over land used previously for training by our platoon.

Three unusual types of weapons were the Northover Projector, the Spigot Mortars and the Smith Gun. They were all cheap mass produced anti-tank weapons, designed to fire a variety of bombs. I believe that they were only issued to Home Guard units. We built a strongpoint at the entrance to Queen Elizabeth Park, Farnborough to enable us to fire either way along the A325. We distrusted pillboxes which sprang up all over the country in 1940 and remain to this day. Once in, you were trapped. It is illustrative of the conditions accepted during those war years when one recalls the Northover practice on a Sunday morning, using a wooden dummy Molotov cocktail was fired down the A325 to check on our line of fire. A corporal was stationed at the road junction at Farnborough Station and the Ship Inn to divert traffic round Ship Lane and Highgate Lane. There wasn't much traffic, but nobody argued and the police didn't require their authority.

In the larger cities, Home Guard units were set up to support anti-aircraft defence. They managed rocket units called 'Z' batteries. Their effectiveness has not been widely published to my knowledge, but it must have given some moral incentive to those soldier/civilians to join in having a crack at the perpetrators of the nightly torment of the Blitz.

Occasionally we were marched as a Church Parade to the Old Parish Church for a service. During the war they were the only times I managed

x - Ivor and Freddy in 1943.

to go to Church. Weekends, particularly Sundays, were HG duty days – the rest were work.

By now the Home Guard was becoming a potentially effective reserve arm of the army. I recall for a while they were the guard at Buckingham Palace. The image presented by "Dad's Army" on television was not true to life in the main although amusing incidents occurred and if rolled into one would produce a similar impression. There was a more serious and truthful side to it all however not portrayed by the media subsequently. Most HG members treated their contribution very seriously and gave much time and in some cases, their lives in an effort to do their bit. (On Remembrance Sunday 1994, in the Westminster Abbey Garden of Remembrance, there was a plot dedicated to the Home Guard). There was no pay and little or no redress in the event of injury or death. Long hours at work, with several evenings training, Sunday morning parades and exercises, all night guards and sometimes courses with the army left precious little time for family, recreation or even sleep; and it went on for 4½ years! It must also be remembered that the working man generally did a six day week additionally in his regular employment. This was nothing in many cases as compared with the regular and enlisted servicemen and women, but the long war years took a toll in fatigue of the whole population, living on meagre ration diets. No. 4 Platoon moved to a new headquarters in a house called 'Estorel', since demolished, near the Ship Inn. We used the approach to the Farnborough Council

Cemetery, a wide road some 100 yards long as our parade ground. I was made Sergeant and then given a commission as a 2/Lt i/c the Battle Platoon. I believe I was the youngest officer in the Battalion.

I discovered problems of leadership very early. As a young officer I considered on one occasion that drill was by no means Coldstream Guards standard. I was holding my short leather covered cane and to emphasise my disapproval in front of some 50 men, I banged it on the side of my leg. Unfortunately it eventually it hit my funny bone and a rather undistinguished gasp and sagging of knees resulted as the pain registered.

A second incident happened on my return from a battle drill course. I wanted to demonstrate how to cross a stream or small river with only one man getting wet. One unfortunate private was detailed to wade Cove Brook near the then hump-backed bridge near the New Inn. The stream is quite wide at that point.

The lad took a toggle rope with him and tied it to the low branch of a tree. He swung the rope back to me on the near bank. The platoon watched while I put my Sten gun sling over my head with the gun on my back. I grasped the rope and swung across the brook. Unfortunately the rope twisted during my flight. I reached the far bank travelling backwards. The gun hit the bank and winded me, and I fell into the water. The platoon discipline was excellent, they did not laugh – well not out loud anyway!

The advent of the Battle Platoon made up for some of the unhappiness at being retained in a reserve occupation. I was given command of some 30 younger men who were also in reserved occupations, or who had been in the forces then withdrawn because their skill would have been wasted in the services. By the time No. 4 Platoon was formed, compulsory Home Guard service was required of all eligible males. This was not greeted with great enthusiasm by the Volunteers and we found that although many were keen to play a useful role, some were just awkward and did not contribute much to the efficiency of the force.

As the war dragged on we received Sten guns, a Browning heavy automatic rifle, bayonets, battle dress, proper badges and other kit, including greatcoats. Our main problem was transport. Army trucks were provided for range practice and exercises, but we did much of our travelling on foot, marching many miles on occasion. We kept rifles, ammunition and sometimes other weapons at home. Bombs were generally kept in the headquarters but even they were kept under the bed in some circumstances to allow a rapid muster. On 'D' Day I had a rifle, Sten gun, ammunition and two 36 type grenades under my bed. Battle Platoon training contained a lot of exhausting fieldcraft, much of it at night. The men appeared to enjoy it and did not complain when wet through, tired and hungry. During one such exercise, I slid accidentally up to my thighs in a cesspit. My mother was most upset when I put my uniform in her linen cupboard to dry out.

No. 4 PLATOON, "A" COMPANY, 27th HAMPSHIRE BN., HOME GUARD, 1944

xi - F.S.S. Front row, 6th from the left - Lt Sam Weller centre.

The regular army was detailed to give us "battle inoculation". Our first experience of this was provided by a local battalion of the Royal West Kent Regiment. We went out to the Long Valley, Aldershot and were given a tactical exercise while machine gunners fired at us with Bren guns aiming some three or four feet from our feet. On the first occasion, a sunny summer's evening (1942 I think), as we struggled to get through a Dannet wire entanglement, my brother Ivor got his rifle sling caught in the barbed wire. He could not pull it free. The gunner thought he would urge him on by firing just above our heads into a tree. Ivor took off pulling the roll of barbed wire with him!

I remained with 'A' Company, even after joining the RAE which had its own unit 'B' Company. I felt that my own unit offered more military stance. However, I was given charge of a mixed platoon of both companies and sent on a week's attachment to join the 7th Wiltshire Regiment at Shoreham. We travelled by train to Brighton and were then billeted in an empty suburban style housing estate in Shoreham. I was given an Army batman or at least I shared one! He scrounged lots of things for me including a bed. We learned a lot during that week and had to experience the same training as the army. We watched the Wiltshires give the Pioneer Corps battle inoculation round a disused farm on the South Downs. We then repeated the exercise with live mortar fire in our support. We used live ammunition to fire at dummies. I was surprised to find that none of us had shot one of our own kind at the end of the day. There were near misses however.

While watching the Pioneer Corps go in before us, the 3 inch mortars were firing over our heads. One bomb landed just behind us but did not explode. The charge did not fire properly. It did not go high enough for the detonator to fire in the long grass, much to our relief.

While being given revision on the Sten gun, a Wiltshire sergeant admonished a Home Guard in my lot for not cocking the gun when loaded. The early model would fire without assistance of the trigger if knocked unless it was cocked properly. He illustrated the point by nearly shooting the man. The gun fired and most of a magazine emptied itself into the ground between the Home Guard's feet without touching him. Unfortunately for the Sergeant his near fatal error was witnessed by a Wiltshire Regiment Captain who quietly took him apart.

We marched many miles in full kit, some of us completing the journey carrying privates' weapons as well as our own since some of the men were hobbling with foot blisters. A strange concept was to make us march through the streets during periods of enemy air activity as anti-aircraft batteries fired overhead and bits of shells would land around us, to give us further experience of being under fire.

We were dumped in the South Downs one evening by truck and left with rations of fresh raw meat, rice, vegetables. The rice was very hard. I thought I could cook rice but without soaking it, the result was hard as bullets. I was entrusted to feed the men then take them back to camps on foot across country overnight. The exercise went well but for one thing, I told the men how to cook the rice, but I forgot the soaking bit and they did not forgive me, for the resultant meal was rock hard. Copies of relevant orders regarding the attachment are enclosed in the appendix.

Soon after I received my commission, I was sent on a week's course for officers. The school was housed in a large house on a park-like estate near Dorking. I travelled by train with my kit and was transported to the establishment which was run by the army. The week seemed to be a miniature Sandhurst type compressed programme. Everything from improving command of troops on the parade ground, tactical exercises, and weapons etc to learning how to cope in the mess at dinner etc! "Mr Vice, 'The King'" would be the call and the rest followed. It was very good and made me even more disturbed at not being allowed to enlist because of my occupation.

It is strange what sticks in the memory after a long time. I well remember how annoyed I was when scaling a stone wall I scratched the brass loop on my web belt. A lot of elbow grease was needed to put it right again to its previous glory.

After my return to Farnborough from Dorking, I was riding my bicycle in civilian clothes, after visiting Renée. As I crossed the main

Farnborough Road on leaving Highgate Lane, I was hit by a Canadian despatch rider on a Harley Davison motorbike. My bicycle was struck behind me and bent right round. The Canadian, a Lance Corporal Pettigrew, was shaken up and I had to write his report for him. I am sure that the course I had been on had given me strength not to panic. We never heard any more. I believe that the despatch rider had been posted elsewhere.

I also attended an exercise at RAE for officers of the Company with Army officers as instructors. We had an exercise presented on a sand table representing the battlefield. At one point the instructor asked what we would do if a certain tactical situation arose from the scenario he had outlined. He asked each of us to give an answer and explain our choice. When he asked me I told him my assessment and gave my reason as not wishing to divide my force. He said, "What is your job?" I told him I was at the Establishment. He said, "You have missed your vocation." That made me feel really bad since my desire to get into a regular unit was underlined and frustrated.

As 1944 began to draw on the Home Guard were stood down. We all felt the bottom of our world had dropped out. There was a huge parade on the large parade ground at South Camp Aldershot as a stand down ceremony. All in greatcoats we marched past the CO. Our Battalion of the 27th Hants Regiment Home Guard must have been well over 1000 strong. We had changed from the 25th to 27th Battalion during the move to Estorel and from 2 to 4 Platoon.

I applied for a commission in the Army Cadet Force but despite a good recommendation from my CO there apparently was no vacant post available.

Chapter 4

WARTIME MINI BOFFIN

By June 1941 I was Head Boy at the Farnborough Grammar School studying for a Higher School Certificate in Science and Mathematics having done very well previously in my Matriculation in 1939. I was RSM of the two cadet companies and everyone was pleased except me. My friends were leaving, there was a big war on and Home Guard and acting as the Air Raid alarm sounder for the school really did nothing to relieve a feeling of wanting to get on with something more exciting. As mentioned earlier my Engineering Drawing master suggested that, until I could attend a Sandhurst exam for the army, which was still operating, he could get me a temporary job at the Royal Aircraft Establishment as a Laboratory Assistant, despite protestations from my Physics Master, Mr R.H. Smith and my father, I agreed. The RAE duly invited me to an interview and, on the 9th June, full of expectations, I was escorted to 70 Building at Farnborough and met by a Mr Robert Whelpton – later to become my Divisional Superintendent and Churchwarden.

The interview was quite short and comprised a short explanation by me of my ability to do anything, and the obvious realisation by him that I knew nothing of the practical world of advanced technology. Responding to his probing to find my preference, which I clearly pointed out was to work on aircraft or machine guns, he indicated that they had just the job for me at an outstation called North Court. RAE had set about dispersing itself after the air raid on the Establishment the previous August when my brother and I experienced a near at hand taste of enemy action.

The afternoon of 9 June was wet. I rode in the back of a Humber shooting brake some 10 miles north of Farnborough. As we travelled further away from the airfield, I wondered if I had made a mistake. I thought of the Tiger Moth flying round the RAE before my interview. Nobody talked to me in the vehicle. Still I was going to get £2.5/-. a week and that couldn't be bad.

The Scientific Civil Service had me in its grasp and to my surprise I was introduced to my new boss, Mr R.C. Bookless, father of a school friend in the sixth form. Reg Bookless had been with the Radio Department since the 1920s. It is of interest to note that I can clearly recall my contacts with many members of the Department, who are listed in the official family tree of 1932. There were some extremely clever and charming people among them. Radio Department was then known as the Experimental Wireless (10 Department)., I knew 20 of the total strength of about 40. To learn that I was to be in Radio was an alarming piece of news. I was getting further away from aircraft. He told me that I was to file contract

50

documents. This I could not believe! I was shown cabinets full of jumbled up documents and told to sort them out. That evening Renée and I sat on the Mounts seat and she listened loyally to my sad tale. I wondered how to pack up and dash off to the Army straight away.

However in the weeks that followed, boring as it was, I began to learn about a new world, of things that the man in the street did not hear about. Radio location, (the code name RDF, Radio Direction Finding, was used to refer to much of what would be termed radar subsequently), was mentioned and such things as Chain Stations, Ground Control, Very High Frequency Radio and things that had contributed in such great measure to victory in the Battle of Britain, the year before. Naturally I had no idea how any of this stuff worked or what it looked like but I was staggered to be apprised of the mass of equipment being made on countless contracts all over the country, in big factories, small workshops and even in backrooms.

I was duly enrolled in the Rescue Squad and periodically about half a dozen of us had to swing pseudo casualties out on derricks and stretchers from the upper floors to the garden below. One of our team was a pretty blonde, one of the three Lake sisters. We would put her in splints then swing the poor girl out into space then lower her on to the lawn. We had our lunches cooked in the kitchens of this old manor house. The Department was headed by a Royal Air Force Officer, a Group Captain Chandler. On one occasion my wages didn't arrive so, with no further hesitation, I asked for an audience and for my money when I was ushered in to see him.

The mobilisation of HM Armed Forces was matched by a mobilisation of the Scientific Civil Service. They came from many walks of life and were called up from the science teacher fraternity, from radio amateurs and even an ex-Imperial Airways radio operator, Frankie Hart. More about him later. The Radio Department alone included some 800 staff at its peak. Chandler was succeeded by a civilian called Philips. He had succeeded Group Captain, later Air Commodore De Burgh who was tragically lost in the Atlantic during a wartime crossing by air. It is believed that several crew were found in a dinghy but had not survived. A memorial plaque commemorated De Burgh's leadership of Radio Department. De Burgh was appointed Head of Experimental Wireless Department in February 1936 as a Squadron Leader. He is listed as a Flight Lieutenant in 1932

Some relief from the utter boredom of filing contract documents for a keen healthy nineteen year old came one day with an instruction to report to a Mr Lax, head of one of the design drawing offices at Farnborough for an urgent short job. His son, Tony, was my close school friend. The mystery was uncovered when I was shown plans of a German U Boat. Mr Lax knew that I made models as a hobby and could work quickly with balsa wood. The woodworkers could produce beautiful models in hardwood, given time. I was set to work immediately and within a few days had made and painted a 3ft long model. I was thanked and it was taken away for a trial of some sort, but I was never told just what it was.

I was soon advised that contrary to any of my aspirations I could not be released for service in HM Forces, even my later call for a medical was squashed. We used to be taken to North Court in lorries each day, standard RAF pattern with a knotted rope to assist access over the tailboard. Ladies had a better means of getting aboard but they had to travel separately in their own vehicle. We were picked up at the Clockhouse Farnborough each day. Since the system seemed unable to arrange more excitement for me, I decided to do something about it for myself.

A Technical Officer called Kinsey, a big Yorkshire radio dealer, was part of the Bookless empire. He knew his way around so I asked him if there was any other slot into which I could fit. He suggested Johnnie Stewart's group at Ambarrow Court, another outstation manor. He thought I might get nearer to aircraft there. How to do it was the next problem. When war broke out, all scientific, technical and industrial staff were kept working every day of the week. Performance deteriorated rapidly, so a day off every eight days was introduced, with staggered rostering. This did not work well and by the time I joined, a six-day week was operating. The staff members could choose to work either Saturday or Sunday. My Home Guard duties were too good to miss and they came most evenings, sometimes all night and on Sundays. I therefore elected to work on Saturdays. It is of considerable interest that one required very little sleep. Air raid alerts, guard duty, fire watching and work itself appeared to require endless effort. There was little grousing on that score by anyone of any consequence. On return from a weekend, as the convoy of lorries arrived at the Clockhouse, en route to the various outstations, I boarded the Ambarrow one. On arrival at Ambarrow, near Crowthorne, I went in to the large entrance hall and into a laboratory which had been the dining room complete with large open hearth and a fire burning brightly in it. A Scotsman, George Hosie, asked me who I was and what did I want. I told him that I had just joined the section. With no further questions he asked me to put some covers onto a grey box with 57 retaining screws while explaining to me that this was an equipment which identified an aircraft to the radio location officer as British. It was an IFF (Identification Friend or Foe) Mark II N, mainly for naval use. I was interested to note that it had been built by Ferranti and it contained an interesting mechanical frequency sweep mechanism, thermionic valves and components which were isolated from the chassis in some cases with folded pieces of blue paper! The condensers were wax covered. The middle of the equipment was taken up with space for a destructive charge for detonation in case of imminent capture by the enemy. In the event this did not appear to deter the enemy because the British in turn captured a German IFF and sent it to us for test; it was a virtual copy of ours.

Johnnie Stewart was a small Scotsman, with a cast in one eye, a shock of hair, recruited from Ferranti up north, he could get very excited. He was very clever however, as were most of the members of his group. Several went on to become extremely senior after the war, but in early 1942 Trevor Moss and John Mills who became Directors of the Royal Radar Establishment, were Junior Scientific Officers or slightly senior. Hubert Gent, Miss Mackenzie, Di Rees, Albert Porter, Leonard Bounds, Dick Walker and Frankie Hart also Jean Brinkworth were all welded into a team developing and testing what we would now know as airborne radar in its early phases. I was quickly introduced to the latest Airborne Interception MK IV and the MK V equipments being used to counter night bombing. They equipped the Beaufighter. The Anti-Surface Vessel ASV Mk II was also the responsibility of the group as design authority.

The staff members were extremely kind and gave me a crash course in all of the mysteries of this new world, absolutely unknown to the world outside.

I confirmed my illegal transfer by phoning Personnel Department at Farnborough and asked them to send my wages to Ambarrow in future, which they did. I heard no more from North Court; I have never discovered what Reg Bookless did about it, if anything.

I joined a class which assembled in ˚No 3 Building at Farnborough to be instructed in radio technology by a little RAF Sergeant. It was the oldest known building connected with aviation in the United Kingdom, despite its enormous bulk of grey corrugated iron (a relic of Cody days), a veritable rabbit warren of corridors and rooms with temporary partitions. The Sergeant showed us films in cartoon form illustrating the electrical properties of thermionic valves. We called these lectures and films "Spots before the eyes".

I soon fell under the guidance of Dick Walker, a lean, young grey-haired technical assistant with a turn of phrase that would make a sailor blush. He became a champion angler after the war but in his spare time at Ambarrow masterminded the collection of Flemish giant rabbits which were reared in the gardens to augment the meat ration. He delighted in inviting the girl typing pool to look at the does and would then let Billy the Buck loose much to the embarrassment of the typists.

Within two weeks I was advised that none of the group considered flying as a sensible pastime and since I was keen I was just the chap they needed. I was packed off for a medical with Sceptic Sam Saunders, the chief medical officer. (Sam Saunders predecessor apparently was called "Gangrene Gordon"). I was so keen that I ran from the ferry car when it got to Farnborough to ensure that I would not arrive late at the Medical Department which was situated in an underground air raid bunker. Sceptic sounded my chest and asked if I was afraid of Doctors, because my heart was beating fast. I explained that it was because I had been running and that it was important that I should be cleared to fly as an observer up to at least 20,000 ft because of the job I was to do. He told me that I should get airborne, see how I got on at 10,000 ft then report back and he would increase the altitude 5,000 ft at a time. A sort of elimination process. There was no indication of the procedure should I not survive at one of those attitudes.

I then reported to Jimmy Lewis, the Departmental Flight Liaison Officer, a chap with a gammy foot. He took me to the ''A' shed parachute room where Mrs Williams and Miss Sheffield fitted me with a harness, gave me a parachute pack, told me what to pull and what not to pull and I was taken to a Beaufort (N1095) in front of 'A' shed. Warrant Officer, Walter Wellwood, later Squadron Leader and Captain, British South American Airways was the pilot. He showed me where to sit and said, "If I pass you going towards the exit, follow me and jump out." He had a young fellow from another department up with him. That flight on 15 April 1942, a lovely April afternoon, was thrilling with an exciting view of a black Whitley and camouflage Lysander flying past us. The one flight was the end of my training and I was immediately conscripted into a team to test an intercom system in a Wellington (T2969). With earphones on about eight of us sitting along the fuselage on anything strong enough not to let us fall through the fabric covering, we took off with the head of the installation section, W.T. Davis (I often wondered if his initials stood for Wireless Telegraphy) calling words to us like "dog, log, jog, wood, should, etc" which we had to write down. I couldn't see outside at all, so for a second flight and first experience of trials work it made quite a change.

On returning to Ambarrow, I was given my first real job. I was introduced to the AI Mk IV and its operation, then shown how it went into a Beaufighter Mk I. A signal generator was fitted onto the floor below the observer's indicator to permit a calibrated pseudo echo to be displayed alongside the real echo. Reference to the attenuator controls in the signal generator allowed a calibration of the signal strengths of the echoes to be recorded. My third flight, about 5.30 pm on a sunny evening with Flight Lieutenant McCracken in a Beaufighter Mk I, X7672, in its sombre black livery was my opportunity to get to real grips with practical science. The money spent on the experiments seemed inordinately greater than my 45/- per week pay. Things seemed to work satisfactorily until we landed on what is now the main runway 26. There was a screeching sound, a violent swing right off the runway straight towards the 'A' shed tarmac littered with parked aircraft. With a terrible smell of burning rubber we stopped among them not touching one. I unlatched the exit under my feet and leapt out only to be dragged back. I had not undone the clip on the monkey wire attached to the D ring on the parachute harness. A very painful experience since the critical piece of the harness passed between the legs. We had burst a tyre, possibly it had deflated on take off. On a succeeding flight, the hatch below my feet opened when I did not have the monkey wire attached, nor had I my parachute pack on, it was normally placed in a housing and only clipped onto the chest before jumping. This was common to all excepting pilots who had seat type

xii - Bristol Beaufighter NF Mk.1 as on my third flight.

parachutes although some pilots used chest types on operations in certain aircraft. The door opened when Di Rees was in the back with his jacket placed on the floor. It fell out. To everyone's amazement it arrived back in Farnborough minus the wallet.

The first experiment proper needed two aircraft, me in the Beaufighter and a target which was a North American Havoc, a night fighter derivative of the Boston day bomber. At some 10,000 ft, we settled down behind the target. The signals took some sorting out among the noise. Earth returns 10,000 ft range coincided with our height. The first attempt started on 8 May 1942 with our Beaufighter just behind the Havoc. A large return was visible. After getting Martindale to slow down to increase the separation between the two aircraft, he gradually lost sight of it. We tended to avoid radio communication since the Germans were not far away and could have listened in. Eventually we lost him and had no way of telling him. I remember that on returning we descended over Lyme Regis and flew back below cliff top height along the coast to avoid detection. We had no guns or Mae Wests. Not all of the coast was prohibited at that time and I recall the look of surprise of two old people on deck chairs on the beach as we rounded a headland only feet from them. The Beaufighter was extremely quiet.

The experiment was interesting and I believe of real value, but it came to an abrupt end in Beaufighter X7672. I was flying with Roly Falk, the O.C. Radio Flight and later Chief Test Pilot of Avro. As we taxied back into Dingley Dell on the south side of the airfield we were met by a row of test sets which Frankie Hart had set out in front of a Hudson for a comparative test. Roly saw these rather late but applied brakes. Nothing happened. He opened up the port engine and turned, then opened up the starboard engine. It coughed and faded, probably a rich cut. We carried on round and collided head on with another Beaufighter doing each no good at all. I looked up to see large chunks of the other Beaufighter descending from above me having been thrown up by our propellers. This time I remembered the D ring. Our ground foreman, Tom Poulter, saw it all and said that I came out from under the Beau like a rabbit out of a burrow and ran up the hill just in case of fire. There was none. Roly just stayed in his seat cursing. It is of interest to note that the Wireless and Electrical (W&E) flight diary recorded this accident in July 1942 but my own log entry is 3 June 1942.

An eminent scientist of later years was Cooke-Yarborough. In the 1942 era he was very much concerned with the design of Monica, a tail warning device, which was intended as a warning system for bombers. It had a unique construction, like the covers on a book for ease of servicing. Unfortunately it proved of more help to enemy night fighters than bombers in service later on. When we were involved however we needed to know what sort of effect a typical fighter would produce in a tail attack. Monica was installed in a Wellington, and, kitted in full Sidcot suit and boots, etc., I sat in the tail turret of the aircraft while a Hurricane made dummy attacks on us. Again no radio between us. I was entrusted with the running commentary of the Hurricane's angle of attack and range. On one sortie I had been giving my accurate account for some time when someone came aft to attract my attention. The intercom had broken down and I had been talking to myself.

Our work required rapid learning, cut and try techniques and quick results. An idea one week would produce an in-service trial the next. I recall a measuring device devised by Dick Walker which tended to oscillate every time he approached it. So he put it on the lawn at Ambarrow and observed the field strength meter through field glasses while standing in the laboratory.

A virile young man, called Gareth Morgan, next commandeered my services to help him with a device used for calibrating the ground radio location 'Chain' system on the south coast. We built a test equipment for installation in one of the Blenheim Mk IV aircraft of No. 75 (Calibration) Wing at Biggin Hill. We originally tried it in some Rotor aircraft, the military version of the Cierva C30 autogiro, based at Halton. Although I stayed there a while and enjoyed the life in the mess I never had the opportunity of a flight. The Biggin Hill situation was different however. Our equipment seemed to work fairly well and a Blenheim IV (Z6085)

xiii - Bristol Blenheim Mk.IV

duly arrived at Farnborough flown by a Flight Lieutenant Jock Shillito. We fitted the kit and flew to Biggin Hill, with Gareth enjoying a ride in the rear gun turret swinging it to and fro. We returned in another Blenheim IV N3598 piloted by Sergeant Doug Houslay. It was decided that an operational trip over the Channel was necessary and that I should be included. However in case we were shot down I was to wear my Home Guard uniform. Since a large number of RAE staff were in the Home Guard or Civil Defence, it was a very common sight to find many of them in battle dress while at work. After some trial runs we set off one afternoon in Z6085 between layers of cloud. I began operating the equipment but was alarmed to hear gunfire only to be told our gunner was just warming up. After a while we suddenly started streaking for the English coast near Rye since our New Zealand pilot, Jock Shillito was advised that bandits were on their way. I was told they were four Focke Wolfes. (I learned some time later that Jock and his crew were killed when their Blenheim's engines failed just after take off and they fell into the valley just south of Biggin Hill). As we crossed the coast the three crew lit cigarettes, I casually asked if that was permitted and was given a very rude reply. I was lodged in the Sergeants Mess with Doug and shared a room with a young Spitfire pilot. We had bunks. When I went in to tea the WAAF gave me a boiled egg, a wartime luxury. She said that I was entitled to it having flown on an operational trip. The mess seemed to have one good gramophone record, the Warsaw Concerto. It was played over and over again by the Spitfire pilots.

It was sad to see the remains of the blitzed pre-war hangars at Biggin. The fighters would set off on sweeps (Rhubarbs) over France while I was there.

Doug would confide that he was not too keen on flying. We would go into Bromley to the cinema; I remember seeing the Great Mr Handel in Technicolour. When coming in to land on one occasion as I sat in the Blenheim turret, Doug said, "this is going to be an awful landing, Freddy!" and he was absolutely right. He would fly a Tiger Moth to keep his hand in. I longed for a flight in one but didn't manage it. Years later, by coincidence I took my Assistant Flying Instructor rating test with Alan (Bunny) Bramson at Biggin Hill in a Tiger Moth.

Ambarrow Court was built near an ancient barrow or burial site alongside the Guildford to Reading railway line. On one hot summer's day the woods and bracken covering the barrow were set alight by a passing steam train. All the staff turned out to douse the flames. We became very rural in our pursuits. Mushrooming in the adjacent fields was a popular pastime as was gardening to augment our food supplies. The old kitchen garden was divided into allotments. When the needs of the electronic war increased, the Air Ministry decided that temporary laboratory buildings should be built on the garden. It produced an instant protest from the gardeners, but despite their protests, officialdom had its way. One of the better gardeners was Wilfred Jackson, and a well named colleague called 'Curly' Kale.

We had some colourful attachments to our airborne equipment group. A young Indian called Desai would spend much time trying to keep warm in front of the fire. We also had three lieutenants from the US Army Signal Corps, Jones, Howden and Beal. They were very attractive to the lady staff members with their pink pants and their interesting stories. A certain blonde divorcee looked after the stores in the entrance hall. She constantly pestered the three officers, hindering their work. They solved the problem by nailing her down in a packing case. Her screams attracted the British and we released her; but on the notice board next day was a warning from G.L. Hunt who was responsible for Ambarrow staff that all such behaviour in future must cease.

A less important misdemeanour was the placing of rabbits in cathode ray tube crates for transit. Johnnie Stewart was furious one morning when he casually opened the front of a crate on a shelf to look at a tube and a rabbit stuck its head out.

George Leslie Hunt became deputy head of the Department in later years but in 1942 he headed the thermionic valve group and indeed he was the foremost authority in valve technology. He occupied the lodge at Ambarrow. That small house appeared to be crammed full of valves. They were so important to our work. One recalls the EF50 in its red can used by the thousand particularly for amplification. The transmitter power triodes generating radiation in the metre waveband were used in the AI transmitters prior to the introduction of the magnetrons and other devices. We coupled two AI transmitters together to provide an early jammer which we fitted into a Wellington after working on it with Frankie Hart through the Easter weekend.

Another team member was a chap called Hunter. He worked on an equipment for measuring distance from a beacon. It was called Rebecca and was the forerunner of the present Distance Measuring Equipment, DME. Range was measured on a vertical time base displayed on a cathode ray tube. Our deputy boss was Horwood, a charming man who had been a schoolmaster, I believe. He later wrote a book on electrical engineering which he gave me to edit. A constant pillar of support, he taught me a lot, not the least how to handle staff to get the best out of them.

The Group returned to G1 Building at Farnborough where as a boy I found the derelict Bristol Fighter, mentioned in an earlier chapter. Soon after we arrived in G1 we were all put on a very special project in readiness for a 1000 bomber raid with as many aircraft as possible equipped with the new hyperbolic navigation aid called 'Gee'. It had been designed by a man called Bowen, who eventually departed for Australia. Twelve equipments were handmade in G1; industrial production had not yet started. Senior Technical Officers such as Horwood and others actually soldered the circuits. My task was very menial. I had to go down to Farnborough Station periodically to collect components not available in the RAE stores. It seemed a strange use of effort since the more junior of us such as young Ford, Singleton junior and others were more in practice at circuit building than the people actually put to work on the bench. We discovered only later what the exercise had really been all about.

The wartime environment precluded the use of some of the sophisticated test apparatus in use today. To ensure that prototype equipment could withstand shock and vibration, a standard test was to roll it down the main Ambarrow staircase. We had one load of test sets fall off a handcart on the airfield tarmac. They all survived. I recall that in later months we received an ASV Mk II indicator which had been thrown out of the rear cockpit of a Swordfish aircraft in service with the Royal Navy. A frustrated observer had, for some reason, decided that his equipment was not serviceable. He unplugged it and heaved it over the side. When we received it, it was of parallelogram shape. The cathode ray tube was broken of course but many of the EF50s were serviceable.

Since the war there have been many histories of radar development. I have found no references to the part played by the RAE in those books and reports. Other establishments particularly Telecommunications Research Establishment (TRE) have been accredited with honours in that direction. Indeed TRE and others played a very major role, but in the early days a considerable contribution was made by the RAE. In addition to all of the work on AI, up to the Mk VI, ASV Mk II, IFF up to the Mk III GR, Monica, jamming systems and some of the early counter-counter measures, a lot of work on ground systems such as the design of aerial towers, Ground Control Systems (GCI), Portable Radar Systems and anti-submarine devices generally was done by Radio Department.

In 1943 we were all moved back to Farnborough from Ambarrow and other groups replaced us at the outstation. We were accommodated in

G1, an old World War I building just outside the RAE itself at Farnborough in Elles Barracks, occupied by the 55th Battalion Royal Tank Regiment. This was a very different atmosphere to that enjoyed previously.

Interestingly enough we were joined by two members of the TRE staff, both experts in IFF technology (Boardman and another). Our efforts in the IFF field were increased and I was employed more in this work than hitherto.

Other jobs intervened however, one of these was the design and construction of a device called Vixen. It was a simple device, a Radio Frequency attenuator for use in an anti-submarine aircraft which had detected a submarine on ASV. To prevent the submarine diving after it had intercepted the ASV signals, the Swordfish or Wellington ASV observer would attenuate his signal progressively as the target was approached. The U Boat crew would conclude that the aircraft was not approaching them. An interesting post-war conversation with a German scientist at a NATO dinner revealed that he had been responsible on behalf of the opposition to discover what we were doing and how we did it.

One of my most memorable jobs was as part of the team to design and develop the original ancestor of the sonobuoy. It was called Wirebasket. The object was to provide a buoy which could be dropped from an ASV fitted Swordfish when it discovered a U Boat. The buoy would be dropped and an attacking aircraft would home onto the buoy using ASV to interrogate the radiated signals from the buoy and thereafter reduce the search area before making an attack. The prototypes were made in G1 of tinned steel and consisted of a 5 foot long tube some 8 inches diameter. The beacon was a converted Walter air sea rescue type as carried by pilots in their dinghy pack. Each Wirebasket contained two telescopic masts. One was fitted with a lead weight and the other erected the oscillator with its dipole aerial. A salt water immersion switch activated the telescopic mast and keel with an explosive charge which was triggered by a circuit once the salt water switch had shorted. The whole contraption was stabilised by a parachute contained in the upper end of the device; the parachute was released by a weighted tape which unwound after the Wirebasket began its descent to the sea. Much workshop and our own effort went into making up these prototypes. A temporary addition to our strength was the arrival of a naval lieutenant commander, an explosives expert. He produced a brew which was packed into the ends of each mast with a 12 second delay for the firing of the charges. The device hit the water, the first charge fired, the lead weight erected the Wirebasket, and twelve seconds later the beacon mast explosive fired and the beacon transmitted drawing power from a battery. Our trials were conducted in a Wellington and the trial area was the Severn estuary. It is difficult to believe in today's atmosphere, but it was considered safer for the RN officer to pack the charges into the units while in flight. He squatted on the Wellington catwalk on our way out west. I then had the dubious task of picking up the whole device, holding it in the flare chute, and on a word from the pilot, usually Walter Wellwood, would push it out into space and wait for some word from the front as to whether it had all worked or not. Di Rees and Albert Porter were positioned in mid estuary to observe the results and to retrieve the rounds. My first offering to the flare shoot rapidly showed signs of an impending disaster. The tape caught in the slip-stream as the tinned steel slowly slipped through my fingers tightly clasped around it. The weight started to unwind and the parachute started to come loose. The intercom advice was that we were starting the run in. I made a quick decision that it was either the Wirebasket or the aircraft, which was fabric covered. I pushed the round out and waited for reactions. It hit the beach near Weston Super Mare. I was told that there were people on the beach but no one was hit and we heard no more about it.

After a few flights things began to sort themselves out. It became a matter of honour to try and hit the boat with Di Rees waving madly as we did a low run past it after the drop. The boat would produce a curving wake as it accelerated away at full throttle as the Wirebasket descended.

Walter surprised me one evening as we turned off down the estuary prior to going home by saying that we had had it. He said that his map must have fallen out of the aircraft and we would have difficulty getting home. I couldn't believe that things were really as bad as that so I began a search around the geodetic structure and found the map tucked in it above Walter's head.

A dramatic demonstration of Wirebasket occurred during a VIP visit to G1. The visitors were shown several rounds lying on the benches. Suddenly there was a loud bang and the lead weight from one came hurtling through the wooden shelves and other equipment, it didn't touch anyone but, true to the wartime reaction, everyone fell onto the floor. The visitors then got to their feet but the staff stayed on the floor and after 12 seconds the other end went off, crashing through the benches at that end. Fortunately no one was touched again but we had to reassure some very frightened visitors.

The Department developed a small dinghy pack radar beacon called Walter. It was a small battery oscillator operating at ASV wavelengths and contained in a cylindrical bakelite case. A wire dipole aerial was attached which opened out upon extraction of the oscillator from its pack. A simple telescopic lightweight mast was extended manually by the pilot once he had got into his K type dinghy. The scheme suited pilots of fighter aircraft since their single seat dinghy could not accommodate the larger transmitter of the multi seat bomber type with its hand operated generator.

Again I was the practical guinea pig. I began trials on the static water tank at Farnborough some 20 yards west of the library. It became a car park eventually. Photographs of me in the dinghy with Walter operating and kitted out in my flying suit were doctored to make it appear I was at sea. The photograph illustrated the operating manual. I then had to get aboard another dinghy on the Solent at Cowes, Isle of Wight. It was very cold and rough. There were no photographers to take the real thing. Present dinghies have double skin bottoms for protection from the cold. The dinghy in service then had no such refinement. I spent two weeks recovering from a chill and flu as a result.

It was about this time that I was introduced to a very exciting job, another demanding the wearing of uniform. Our commandos were being landed by submarine on the beaches of France in twos and threes then being picked up again from their small dhory craft. There was a problem in locating them and it was hoped that Walter would meet the need.

I was sent down to Newhaven kitted up in my 2nd Lieutenant battledress to meet some Belgian Commandos looked after by a British captain in the RASC, surprisingly. I was taken out of the harbour in a dhory by some of these chaps complete with Walter. We did some experiments in collaboration with a motor torpedo boat with a Royal Navy crew. The coastal area was normally prohibited unless you were a resident or in the services and I was interested to see that the MTBs were painted in blue, grey and white. On a fine blustery morning the difficulty of transferring from a little craft on to the heaving deck of the MTB was something I hadn't bargained for. My hobnail boots slid all over the deck even when I eventually got there. I was very cold. The Royal Navy had an immediate answer which nearly knocked me for six while warming me up, a very large tot of rum.

I spent several days on this exercise living in a small hotel with the others, or some of them billeted there. I recall the sight of a small commando with glasses and a stocking cap, all kitted up for an operation one evening calmly drinking half a pint of beer before the night's work. We had the odd air raid, I didn't like it at all. While we sat round a table listening one night to the pretty near drone of enemy aircraft, my Captain friend said, "don't worry, son, if one gets too close, I'll be under the table long before you get there."

It was often necessary to fly two observers in the Beaufighters, but there was only one observer seat, under a perspex dome half way down the fuselage. The second observer had to perch him or herself on the armour plate steel edge between the armour plate doors. It was uncomfortable and as there was no safety harness one had to hang on to the sides during take-off and landing. One Saturday afternoon I was due to test an AI Mk VI together with Miss Mackenzie, we called her Nina May. The aircraft, T9470 I believe, was waiting up on Jersey Brow, the present site of the Fire Station. It was camouflaged brown and green and duck egg blue underneath, not the usual nightfighter black. Flt. Lt Hood was the pilot. Nina May was already perched between the armour plate doors when I arrived knitting a sock with three needles and three balls of red wool rolling on the floor making the already complex interior of the aircraft look like a rat's nest.

xiv - F.S. Stringer, all at sea. It was very cold during the real test.

I began a lot of IFF flying, usually monitoring interrogating signals with equipments such as the Mk III GR. Our models were grey but we began to receive American built Chinese copies finished in crackle black and looking very smart indeed. I was joined by Flight Lieutenant Alan Lawrence, seconded from a night fighter squadron as an RAF observer attached to Radio Flight for the purpose. He and his wife Margaret became godparents to our daughter Carol eleven years later. Our pilots were a most expert team. With Roly Falk as O.C. Radio Flight he was supported by Flt. Lt. (later Squadron Leader) E.A. 'Robin' Hood, Bob Martin and Walter Wellwood. 'Guest Artists' included Squadron Leader A.F. Martindale and others. A Polish pilot named Kalpas was in the flight for a while. Flt. Lt. A.W. Fraser DFC was tragically killed together with a team from Radio Department when they had engine failure in a white and grey Wellington (HF 252/G) which failed to reach base. This happened in June 1944. Warrant Officer S. Bickell, a charming man, and two of Radio Department, Mr Parker and Mr Erskine were killed. Mr Dart was injured. Bob Martin had a large black Labrador which flew with him very frequently. In May 1943 Bob had made a forced landing in a Typhoon at Torquay in the water. He broke his arm and nose. After returning from hospital on 28 July the poor man caught chicken pox in September and was on sick leave for another three weeks. The flight moved from the huts occupied by the ˙A shed handling crew into the then new huts adjacent to the also new wartime control tower, the latter stood for many years behind the post war control tower. The huts were eventually demolished. Photographs of the total strength of all RAE pilots over the years adorned the walls of the post war control tower.

Although Beaufighters and Wellingtons were the usual aircraft, I had many opportunities to fly in our Hudson T9433 and the Mosquito. Usually Alan Lawrence and I would do the observing in the Beaufighter and he gradually took on a variety of jobs for our group and others.

The Hudson was used as a small flying laboratory for many tasks, particularly VHF communications. The problem with this American military version of the small pre-war Lockheed 14 derivative of the Electra was that if the undercarriage collapsed, the oleo legs would puncture the fuel tanks and the petrol would flood onto the exhaust pipes resulting in a fire. I watched with baited breath one day alongside runway 11 as a Hudson burst a tyre while gathering speed for take-off. The complete aircraft swung round in a very tight ground loop and continued backwards for a while. The undercarriage didn't collapse.

On the same runway one day we taxied out in a Halifax, the radial engine variety, past the Officers Mess and onto the threshold of what we called the Queen's Hotel runway. I sat waiting for take-off but we didn't move. After a while I called the pilot to enquire why the delay. He said come up here and look. Sitting in the middle of the runway in front of this great four engine bomber, and looking up at it, was a small dog. We had to wait until a van came over from the Control Tower to persuade him to move before we did.

I flew in a Swordfish (K8373) twice on an ASV interference trial in January 1943. Basically it wasn't my experiment but I was required as an extra observer. This aircraft had seen better days and I was surprised to note that it had a Vickers K gun still in its stowed position in the rear cockpit. I learned a little about the aerodynamic force of the slipstream during my second trip. I tried to attract the attention of the pilot by tapping him on the shoulder; my arm was flung back forcibly as I lifted it. The second flight was the aircraft's last. That night there was a gale and as it sprang up it turned the Swordfish over smashing it up. Tom Poulter hung on to the wing tip in Dingley Dell in a vain attempt to save it but was lifted off the ground before letting go I was told.

A sad but very amusing sight was a first attempt to use Rocket Assisted means of getting a Swordfish airborne quickly or with an increased load when flying off aircraft carriers. The scheme known as RATOG was later used extensively. However on the day in question, I happened to be in front of A shed as the experimental Swordfish taxied to the threshold of the main runway. The engine was opened to full power and with a flash and lots of flame and smoke, the rockets were fired. The rear fuselage and tail caught fire and the pilot leapt out and ran. The rest of the aircraft did not catch alight but the poor Swordfish looked very sad. I found it very amusing and laughed only to be told by a very irate gentleman wearing cycle clips to b..... off, and hadn't I got anything better to do. I think it was his project.

IFF gave me the opportunity to fly in one or two exciting types. I was included in a team doing some work on the personal Dakota of General Maitland Wilson. Walter Wellwood flew this beautifully furnished aircraft. I was very surprised to note a cocktail cabinet and other accessories. The trip was marred somewhat by my nursing a painful foot. The huge door slammed on it as Walter opened the port engine.

The most exciting flights were in the Mosquito. For the first time I was actually asked to do something by Bob Martin which affected the aircraft control. He asked me to turn a few switches. The close proximity of pilot and navigator/observer sitting almost side by side had its problems in my case however. Bob seemed a little unsure of his position one day to the east of Farnborough. I casually pointed out that I recognised the Queen Mary Reservoir whereupon he told me that he would do his bloody job and I should get on with mine. The subsequent atmosphere was frigid until we landed. Until recent times there was often an air of superiority of pilots over boffins excepting in some cases where the latter put in lots of hours.

I was privileged to be in a Mosquito when we climbed up near a very large formation of U.S. Army Air Force B17 Fortresses returning from a daylight raid, probably over France since they were flying due north over the Hampshire coast. Someone remarked later that we could easily have had a few rounds aimed in our direction. The approach to land in the Mosquito was interesting. For once the boffin could see ahead and the fine pitch propeller tips near ones ear and an approach speed of 126 mph was reason for a little stiffening of the knee joints.

We still did a lot of flying in the Wellington. I was flying with Robin Hood participating in an IFF Mk III GR trial. There were only the two of us aboard. It was necessary for me to monitor the interrogating aurally which meant unplugging my intercom lead from the aircraft system and plugging it into the IFF. This meant that I would be out of contact with the pilot. Unfortunately I omitted telling him that I was temporarily unavailable. As I concentrated on the trial I saw a movement out of the corner of my eye, situated where I was half way down the fuselage. It was Robin coming towards me looking very fierce. He had been talking to me, but getting no reply. He put the aircraft onto the automatic pilot and came aft apparently to sort me out. I retreated down the catwalk to the rear turret with the object of getting into it. Having told me a few of his thoughts he eventually went back up front. I always remembered to tell the pilot what I intended to do subsequently.

Returning from Salisbury Plain, again in a Wellington, I was passing the time by holding on to the two catwalk hand ropes attempting to do a handstand. A movement outside the fuselage caught my eye and once back to my normal upright position, I was surprised to see a clipped wing Spitfire tucked in to our wing with the pilot looking at me. I turned to call the pilot who was unaware of our visitor when I saw another Spitfire tucked in on the port-side. The pilot of our Wellington kept very steady and asked me to tell them what was happening. The starboard fighter then dropped below us and came up on the other side while his wingman went over us and onto the starboard side. The lower aircraft was so close I could see the pilot holding the control column. They peeled away either side in a flash and were gone. The chaps up front never saw them.

Alan Lawrence accompanied flights to much greater altitudes than I was expected to fly. The Mosquito used was unpressurised. He was thankful for the oxygen supply for an extra reason since the low ambient pressure made the passing of wind an embarrassing hazard. One of the very first Mosquitoes to be used for night fighting came to us in 1943. It was all black and sat outside B shed in the FIE yard. B shed had replaced the old airship shed, one of three originally. During the war the number of hours flown by RAE were painted in thick white lines year by year, a sort of histogram. The hours in 1944 were 8593, about four times the 1940 figure.

A lot of experimental activity with various gliders took place at RAE during the gradual build up to D Day. Small Hotspur gliders were towed by Hectors and Masters, but the larger Horsas and Hadrians were towed by Whitleys. There were three of the latter with a name printed on the nose of each of these otherwise all black aircraft. They were called 'Chattanooga Choo Choo I, II and III' respectively. Hunter had some experiments going in one of the Horsas using Rebecca I believe, but although I managed to inspect his brand new glider I never got a flight in it. The Whitleys sometimes towed two Horsas at a time.

At one period it was decided to use Royal Air Force ground crew to augment the RAE civilian industrial staff. Although they worked hard it appears to have been a mistake. Many accidents happened, some with loss of life, although not necessarily attributable to the ground staff. There were one or two unfortunate instances. The prototype Avro Manchester was dispersed on Jersey Brow when not flying. It was in brown and green camouflage with yellow under surfaces. As the engines were started on its final day, the undercarriage retracted and the aircraft broke its back. The word going round was that someone had selected the up position during a previous unauthorised look round the cockpit. This was the unarmed prototype L7246 according to A.J. Jackson (Avro Aircraft since 1908). It was at RAE for perfecting a catapult launching and arrested landing technique, specifically designed for the Manchester, but in the end, never used. This clearly was the reason for its station on Jersey Brow, the site of all RAE catapults since the inter-war years. Bruce

Robertson's book on British Military Serials states that L7246 became 3422M, an instructional serial, which probably means that despite the accident the aircraft was still used to some purpose. I also recall that Robin Hood had the double tail wheel of an early Stirling collapse on landing, wearing away the bottom of the turret.

In October 1942, Robin Hood (a Flight Lieutenant at that time) was flying Stirling L7605 when the starboard outer engine blew up and caught fire when the flaps and undercarriage were already down. The damage to the tail unit and fuselage occurred during the landing on the airfield under very difficult conditions. Robin became O.C. Wireless and Electrical Flight in July 1943 when he succeeded Squadron Leader R. (Roly) J. Falk who was promoted to the post of Chief Test Pilot.

A starter truck backed into a new and recently refurbished Warwick causing much damage and requiring an immediate return to the hangar. Another Warwick burnt out outside F1 hangar. At the end of the war Alan Lawrence was passing a black and white upper surfaces Lancaster being run up at full power. He was on his way to the mess. The aircraft was pointing at the hangar near Cody's Tree. There was a new noise of a thousand falling tin cans as the undercarriage retracted and the propellers hit the tarmac. Alan said that an RAF airman slowly emerged from the upper hatch over the cockpit to survey what he had done.

In August 1943 I managed a flight in Fortress 25745 which came to RAE for Oboe trials. This was a U.S. Air Force aircraft, all silver and completely armed. The long belts of ammunition all down the fuselage were a surprise also the comparatively small bomb bay as compared to our Lancaster. The ball turret under the fuselage, or rather in the floor, had a notice on it warning that access without proper instructions could result in serious injury. Oboe was a precision navigation aid used by pathfinder units on raids over Germany.

The army had a contingent of officers based at the airfield for several months flying Tiger Moths. Their purpose was not generally understood. We were fascinated to watch one of the aircraft begin a take-off and swing to the right of the main runway. It continued with tail up and full power in a big arc until it finally collided with a bowser just south of Jersey Brow.

There was considerable excitement when a captured German IFF set arrived in G1. It was of the same size and similar shape to our Mk III but painted darker grey and the beautifully constructed interior with cast sub-chassis had that characteristic smell common to all of the German electronics. I flew with it on test flights which resulted in work beginning on techniques to spoof the enemy by using his coding and frequencies.

As mentioned previously, the destructor mechanism on our IFF had clearly not worked in view of the evident copying of our design by the Germans. During the experiments at Farnborough with our destructors it was decided that the cine unit would make an instructional film on the subject. The idea was to show that complete destruction of the interior was effected with no harm coming to the aircrew. We had three RAF men attached; they were housed in a workshop-come laboratory on the high ground just to the west of Stonehenge Road, near Dingley Dell. Corporal Connor and A/C Clynch plus one other comprised the team. Two of them placed the primed IFF on the ground with the set some feet from them near the entrance to 70 building. The cameras turned and the switch was fired. There was a loud bang and the lid of the set shot up many feet in the air. Both airmen ran for their lives; not what was intended. It seemed that radio and explosives did not harmonise well every time that we endeavoured to introduce pyrotechnics.

One of our number after the war was a German scientist who had developed their IFF. On one occasion I was told, his experimental equipment fell out of a Junkers Ju88 much to his consternation.

In the months before D Day the Germans were making raids on the south coast, presumably hoping to disrupt preparations for the invasion. Leonard Bounds had been advised that, because of a lack of trained navigators, the Luftwaffe was employing a master aircraft fitted with an IFF modified to a 'Rooster' mode. This allowed other aircraft to identify it with their own radar. They would then formate on the master to reach the target. RAE managed to modify some British equipments to have the same characteristics as the master. We called this Red Queen.

I was despatched, again in uniform, to Ford airfield in April 1944. The airfield was equipped with the Mk 30 Mosquito with the latest American A1, Mk 8 I believe. It had an orange Cathode Ray Tube (CRT) display with a horizontal sweep time base. I was to modify our sets to provide a Luftwaffe coding and frequency sweep. There were the two Royal Australian Air Force Squadrons on the airfield

The whole area around Ford was swarming with troops, mainly commandos in training. They carried lots of equipment and pulled heavier weapons on two wheel barrows, just a frame with wheels.

I stayed in the Officers' Mess and met some very friendly people. The ground crew were most helpful. To complete the modification required the removal of the loaded Verey pistol from the top of the cabin transparency, then removal of the IFF situated behind it. Each removal required the services of the armourer. Test flights were made by the service crews but one returned with some annoyance having been shot at by our anti-aircraft batteries. The navigator reached for the Verey pistol to fire the colour of the day to find it was unloaded. The armourer had not replaced the cartridge after I had completed my modification. He was put on a charge. I asked to see the C.O. and explained the difficulties and I was told the airman had been excused.

The day before the real operational test of the success or otherwise of this attempt to spoof the Luftwaffe was preceded by the usual Night Flying Tests (NFTs). I recall a very nice Australian crew telling me that everything was working alright. There was an alert that night and the squadron was airborne with one or more of our Mosquitoes radiating the spoof signals. The raiders fell into a neat trap and several were shot down. Rumour has it that the number was twelve but that figure is very suspect and I have never found any proof of it. Nevertheless returning crews were jubilant but to my great sadness one of our aircraft did not return. It was the one with the two nice Australian chaps. We never discovered what had happened to them.

The Germans had been caught once and were twice shy. They didn't attempt such a navigational technique again, so I was recalled home after I had put all of the sets to normal. I returned to Farnborough nursing a severe stomachache caused by eating spring onions for tea in the mess. I was cheered before leaving Ford by a phone call from Leonard Bounds who told me that I had been promoted to Technical Assistant Grade III. At last I had begun to creep up from the bottom rung.

D Day was wet and blustery for June. We heard about it on the early morning news. We had wondered when it would all start and our first reaction was to cadge a flight to have a look. Even the RAF chaps were unsuccessful since, obviously, gash rubberneckers would be most unwelcome. We had a maximum Home Guard muster in case of a counter attack by parachute troops. We all turned out with every bit of armament we had, but no luck, no one came.

While on standby that June evening we watched a large formation of low flying Albemarles towing gliders fly low over the Farnborough Grange on a heading of about 160°. Presumably they were some sort of reserve since the main airborne landings had been completed some fifteen hours earlier.

By my birthday on 15th June the V1 Doodlebugs began their attacks. I was in London the day before. We had been warned by the Home Guard to expect raids by pilotless aircraft. It was some time before we got them over RAE. One flew right down what was runway 29 quite low, its engine stopped nearby but it exploded some way off. Although RAE was liberally supplied with air raid shelters they were seldom used. For V1 attacks we were instructed to ignore the normal air raid sirens and to continue working. Imminent danger was signalled by klaxon horns in each laboratory or building. When they sounded we had to get under the bench then emerge after the missile had gone over or exploded. V2s landed in the Windsor area and surrounding districts without warning but none fell on Farnborough.

As the campaign in Europe began to provide a foothold for our armies so the opportunity came to capture interesting enemy aircraft. Lt. Commander (Winkle) Brown who was an RAE Test Pilot gives a comprehensive account of the retrieval of enemy aircraft in his book. Earlier in the war we had become familiar with the sight of test flying by RAE pilots of an Italian CR42, Focke Wolfe 190s and Junkers Ju88s.

In fact I almost managed a flight in the JU88 but it went unserviceable just before start-up.

In September 1944 RAE received a call for the collection of the first captured Heinkel 177 four-engine bomber. Wing Commander 'Roly' Falk was to take a Hudson (T9433) to France escorted by two Beaufighters. One of these was the aircraft containing experimental equipment in which I had particular involvement. I arrived at 'Dingley Dell' on the airfield one morning to discover that the Beaufighter and another were missing. Robin took mine, probably T4790, which had been cleared of the equipment, and Flt Lt Lance 'Bob' Martin took R2241. (I learned from Pamela Hood that Bob and Robin were brothers-in-law; the latter still lives in the West Country). Upon arrival over an airfield in France after seven hours flying, lights were switched on for the Hudson to land as night had fallen. The Beaufighters did not have the airfield radio frequency crystals on board and their pilots were dismayed when the runway lights were extinguished, leaving them circling overhead and short of fuel. Bob bailed out, but Robin decided that his girth exceeded the escape door aperture behind him. His seat type parachute made an exit somewhat risky, so he crash landed. Both Beaufighters were lost but the 177 (JS439) was retrieved to Farnborough.

Minor injuries put Robin into a French hospital for a few hours. While there he found himself in a ward shared by German prisoners of war. For some unknown reason a German officer came around the ward presenting an Iron Cross to some of the pyjama-clad prisoners; he gave one to Robin, presumably thinking him to be a German!

After Word War II and demobilised in 1945, Robin flew civil aircraft charter work in aircraft such as the Dragon Rapide from White Waltham and later concentrated upon helicopter flying for the Decca Navigation Company. He died some years ago.

The V1s were termed 'divers' by the radar operators, usually Women's Auxiliary Air Force (WAAF). While on duty at an RAF station one evening I was given the opportunity of seeing them coming in, as displayed on the Ground Control Interception (GCI) indicators. Seeing where they were going was sad knowing that any getting through would cause casualties and much destruction. Being under one was a selfish experience, you just hoped that the engine would keep going. That meant of course, that it would cause someone else the misery.

As 1944 progressed Horwood and one or two others gave priority to Counter Counter measures in terms of various airborne equipments.

Our IFF work continued. One late afternoon I went out to a Beaufighter to find the pilot Squadron Leader already in the cockpit so I just saw his back. I had never met him before. We were due to fly against the Sopley radar not far from Bournemouth. We set off towards Sopley and made radio contact and were vectored to fly out over the Channel. I was in civilian clothes, we had no Mae Wests, no dinghy and no ammunition in the guns. We were asked to keep on course. As we got further out over the sea we began to get a bit worried as we were approaching the Channel Isles which were still occupied. Eventually looking down we were just about over the coastline. There was no activity and no anti-aircraft fire. We were actually told to carry on a bit further but by mutual agreement the two of us decided that enough was enough and told Sopley we were returning. It was getting late when we got back to Farnborough and I saw my pilot face to face for the first time.

Some six days after D Day, my brother Ivor's 11th Armoured Division moved out of Church Crookham to the mustering camp in the south east of England. He was a radio operator in a M10 Sherman chassis 17 pounder anti-tank unit of the 75th AT Regiment Royal Artillery. It was an unhappy experience to us all as they moved out past G1 and along the main Farnborough Road. I didn't see Ivor but I knew he was among them. He had a rough war from then on. He was at Caen, Flers, the breakout to Belgium, Holland and Germany up to the Luneberg Heath. He rose to Sergeant before being demobbed after the war. During the cold winter of 1944-45 he came home on leave. After an evening at the local, Renée and I found his sense of humour hadn't changed; he was sitting in his greatcoat on the pillar box saying that he had been 'posted'. As the war in Europe was drawing to a close we began to concentrate on control equipment for IFF and radar operations in the Far East.

Earlier in April 1944, Wellington (BK456) had been kitted up with as much relevant avionics as was likely to be used in the Far East. The aircraft was called 'The Gen Palace'. Robin Hood asked me to make a model of 'The Gen Palace'. I made the 1/72nd fuselage but never finished the complete aircraft. At an SBAC show at Farnborough in 1984, I met Robin who remembered the request and was still interested. The fuselage is still in my possession. The overseas flight covered 18,000 miles over India, Egypt, Iraq, Italy and North Africa in a flying time of 120 hours.

By the spring of 1944 a considerable shake up administratively caused many of our old group to transfer from RAE to TRE at Malvern. Johnny Stewart, Hubert Gent, Jean Brinkworth, Frankie Hart, Dick Walker and Gareth Morgan all left us. The IFF team stayed much to our relief. Another very well known person to go to TRE was John Mills who had participated in original work such as Distance Measuring Equipment. Trevor Moss went too, so did Cooke -Yarborough. Some more junior staff went with them and Horwood became our section chief. Robert Whelpton was the Divisional Head and our Head of Department was Dr. B.G. Gates (who had succeeded Dr. H.M. Barlow), a man with a Jack Hulbert type of chin, who, despite his exalted position came to work on a bicycle. In fact many senior ranks did so. Perhaps the most amusing was the use of horse transport. There was the officer who rode to work and grazed his horse on the edge of the playing field, tethered of course. Another who was a Radio Altimeter king came to the establishment in a pony and trap. Hubert Gent wore a green cloak to and from G1. He walked through Elles

Barracks. This was a most unusual attire for a young man. He never changed it even despite the catcalls and whistles from the open barrack room windows of the 55th Tank Regt. troops.

On one occasion Alan Lawrence, complete with fighter pilot type flying jacket and officer's cap, stared hard at about 60 troops marching under the command of an NCO. Alan, sitting in his jeep, stared at the troops as they gave an eyes right. I nudged him and said, "it's for you." He came back to earth and returned the salute. One of my proud moments was when a Canadian soldier saluted me as I walked along the main road in uniform. It was my first time.

The distance from G1 to the gate of 70 building was some 300 yards. We were continually moving equipment backwards and forwards to and from the airfield. To forestall a rash of pilfering, only too easy between buildings, Mr S, Harrison the Departmental Admin. Officer, decreed that everything had to have a gate pass. This became a time and effort wasting ritual since the policemen on each gate had no idea how to identify equipment, much of which was advanced and classified, so we couldn't tell him anyway. To remove the problem, Frankie Hart suggested that we should tidy the laboratory and put all of the junk scrap material onto a handcart. He then made out a gate pass for a transmitter type 1000, had it authorised and handed in to the policeman as we pushed it to 70 Building and the main establishment complex. He took the lot to P161 Building and said to Harrison, ' so much for your system'. We were excused from further requirement of that sort forever then on.

Several of the buildings which sprang up during World War II to augment the corrugated sheds of the previous war were made of brick and concrete. They included the high speed wind tunnel, *Q134 Building for weapons department and P160 and P161 for Radio Department. Q134 was reputed to have been built on the wrong side of the road because the most attractive side appeared on the south leaving the untidy fire escapes and balconies facing the road. Alternatively it may have been built back to front.

'P160 Building however was purpose-built to provide a shell for two advanced Battle of Britain type operations' rooms. It would have been invaluable some years earlier. As it was, it arrived years too late and was immediately used for a variety of experimental purposes not connected with the original intent. One room became the aerial laboratory and eventually the other became the library. Previously the site had been derelict ground with a muddy path to the airfield.

We had been introduced to the jet era with the arrival of the Gloster E28/29 during May 1943. We were able to watch it flying at much higher speeds than the more conventional types. It was flown by Charles McLure on many occasions. I had the honour in later years of painting a picture of the aircraft for him. My introduction to the type was quite dramatic. As it taxied out one morning from H hangar, I noticed several

RAF policemen with white tops to their caps and white gaiters and belts. They each had a revolver. The strange noise and sight of this very unusual aircraft caused me to walk towards the edge of the tarmac near the control tower. One of the policemen waved me away with his revolver. As soon as it landed the Gloster taxied to H Hangar, which still exists, and was quickly put inside. As time went on there seemed to be the usual relaxation of security.

Squadron Leader W.D.B.S. Davie flew the Gloster for some 21 hours during its first month at RAE. He had to abandon his aircraft during an early jet engine test at 36,000 ft. Having lost his oxygen mask he stuck the pipe in his mouth and survived in a free fall, one of the longest parachute descents on record at the time.

The Meteor in its early versions appeared on the scene before VE Day, also I was surprised to have my first sight of a Vampire. There were several Meteor accidents. On returning along the road from lunch on my bicycle on 4th January 1944, I was attracted to an unusual noise in the sky and saw one of these early Meteors falling uncontrollably with its structure obviously damaged. It fell outside RAE in the swampy wood near G1, now the site of the Industrial Estate. The pilot, Squadron Leader W.D.B.S. Davie, was killed. He fell somewhere near Alexandra Road I believe. The actual aircraft was DG204 with a specification number F9/40. The official explanation was that one of the F2 turbines disintegrated.

VE Day came upon us almost without warning from a job point of view. So quickly in fact, that I turned up for work only to be told by the policeman on duty at G1 that we had the day off. No one was coming in to work. I had not been advised of my formal instruction so with some sense of unease I went home again. I must have been the only one to have tried to work. There was a considerable sense of anticlimax despite the fact that the Far East war was still on. Streetlights had appeared again some weeks earlier and much to our disappointment the Home Guard had been stood down. There was no attempt to reduce the strength of the RAE however, and as soon as we returned to work we were concentrating on the Far East situation. Radio Department had been to the forefront in the development of VHF radio for the 1940 era and earlier and people such as H. Leslie Bennett had produced the combined microphone and oxygen mask essential to victory in the Battle of Britain. A very large project to couple this work with ground radar fighter control absorbed the effort of a lot of the Radio Department staff. The project was called 'Baccy'. The whole system was to be installed in a ship to allow the efficient use of allied aircraft as they operated nearer and nearer to the Japanese homeland. In the event the system was ready in time for VJ Day in August 1945.

The end of the war against Germany caused a bit of a lull in my flying activity until early in 1946. In November 1945 we had an exhibition of German aircraft at the Establishment. It was an amazing collection of captured and surrendered equipment. A full account is given in Eric (Winkle) Brown's book. A newcomer to W and E Flight was Flt.Lt. D.G. Taylor DFC, an ex pathfinder pilot who continued as a test pilot in both W and E and Aero Flights as a civilian after his demobilisation. He transported equipment backward and forwards in a captured Seibel AM28 twin-engine communications aircraft. Flt Lt. Later Squadron Leader G.R.I. (Sailor) Parker DFC joined W and E Flight and became C.O. on Bob Martin's demob. in February 1946. Robin Hood had returned to civilian life the previous November. All achieved Squadron Leader rank.

My activities continued to be concentrated for a while on the various ground radar systems out on the airfield working with Mick Weedon, and the famous Popham. To say the least Pop was a very practical man and despite his rise to senior ranks, invariably dressed in old clothes and was always happy when working with real systems in the field. We were working on a mobile field IFF interrogator. It all went into a tent. It was positioned near the GCI site near the position of the western aircraft gate of the civil enclave at Farnborough. We scattered one fine afternoon when a Master Mk II came off the main runway and headed towards us. At that time Mick Weedon and our famous radio mechanic, Joe, formed part of the project.

Mick and I did a rapid evacuation of our installation upon the unexpected approach at high speed of the Miles Master Mk II. The complex site was kept in running order by Joe. He had become something of a legend at RAE and would turn his hand to anything. It was, and always has been, a characteristic of the RAE, that because of its experimental nature, almost anything could be made or provided by someone if a special need arose. Nowhere was this been demonstrated more clearly than in the various design offices and workshops. The wooden models were always most splendid, indeed we would often get people like Joe to knock some piece of metal or wood together for a quick job since we could not bear to spoil the magnificent piece of work that the workshops would provide if asked. Usually an experiment would result in a change and consequent spoiling of the item.

The arrival of the German aircraft was cause for much test flying to study their performance. One of the most interesting type was the little Heinkel jet monoplane, the 'Volkesjäger'. I walked through the copse one morning in Dingley Dell towards the two new hangars called E3. The scene was almost dreamlike. There were several of these little fighters there, and they were being serviced by ex Luftwaffe ground crew still wearing their service uniforms. One felt a slippage of time and place, it might have been on a German airfield a year or so before.

Many German aircraft were brought back for testing by our pilots. Sadly it resulted in casualties. One of the Volksjäger jets crashed into a barrackroom in Blenheim Barracks and killed the pilot. Group Captain Hards was the Commanding Officer of Experimental Flying Department.

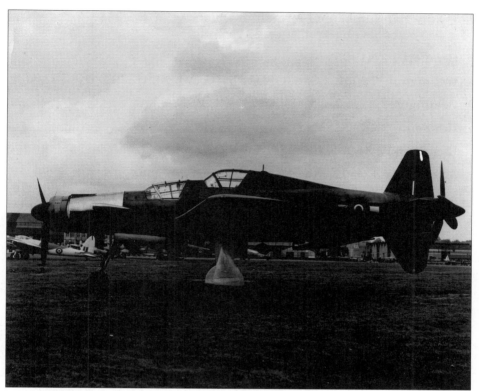

xv - The Dornier Do335 flown by Group Captain Hards.

He was flying the Dornier 335, a strange large night fighter with a propeller at the front and one at the rear. It had a failure and crashed into the playground of an infants' school in Cove. Group Captain Hards was killed – none of the children were hurt, but air testing of the German aircraft ceased from then on.

Serial Numbers of Aircraft in which
I acted as observer during 1942-45:

Beaufort   N1905

Wellington   T2969, Z844/G, HZ579/G (MK X), HZ202, HG 352/G

Beaufighter   X7672, T4790, R2241/G, V8830

Hudson   T9433, AM823, AM865

Blenheim IV   Z6085, N3598

Anson I   EG313, NK141

Swordfish   K8373

Fortress   25745

Mosquito   DZ409, LR328

Halifax III   HX228

Dakota   FZ631

Oxford   P6806

Lancaster   JA876

Dominie   X7490

Chapter 5

POST WAR ERA
RESEARCH & DEVELOPMENT

As the old IFF group broke up after the war and people like Leonard Bounds and Di Rees returned to their old occupations, Mr Horwood moved with some of us from a new organisation within Radio Department to continue a variety of jobs. Some of these involved continuing with the IFF theme doing tests upon a small ground interrogator installed in a small tent near the Ground Control Interception Radar (GCI) positioned where the western end of the new Civil Enclave fence runs. I worked there for a while with Mick Weedon before he went back to college to complete his degree. Our electronic worker – cum handyman, was a ubiquitous and well-known character, Joe Edwards. He always called me String. I don't know how we could have done without him. I was amazed to note that when the job closed, no one bothered to check up on inventory items or to ensure their safety, they were just left.

Returning for a moment to the old G1 period, a very nice chap was called Sands. He was a builder by trade and had been conscripted into the Department because he was a radio amateur. I met him many years later at a Departmental reunion.

Back to the Horwood period, it coincided with my endeavours to improve my scientific and technical knowledge. This came however after I had received a nasty shock while winding up work in G1 of being made redundant. The note was passed to many members of staff and we could see Robert Whelpton as the Divisional Head going round on his bike looking for people. I just avoided him, hoping for the best, not that it would have made the slightest difference. He said I was the best ACIII he had and was very sorry. It didn't cheer me in the slightest. As I rode home to give my young bride the sad news, it started to snow and sleet. I put in for a variety of jobs but most wanted to have me work at a bench making radios. I hated the thought. I went to High Wycombe by bus to talk it over with my father and Uncle Jim who were joint directors of a bakery at the time. Nothing seemed to be going right when I received call-up papers – and the war was over! Within days however I also received notice from RAE that my redundancy was a mistake since the RAE and TRE redundancy, based on time of service, had not matched. I hadn't actually left and found I didn't need to.

So when I left G1 with Horwood I started night school at Guildford Technical College to get City and Guilds qualifications and simultaneously went back to my old Farnborough Grammar School, this time as a night student to catch up where I had left off studying for my Inter BSc. I also took a fourth subject of Geography by correspondence course. It was all a bit trying. However I passed them all in due course getting a Final Telecommunications Certificate of the City and Guilds, also my Inter BSc. which I took in London. Horwood had written a book on Electrical Engineering and he kindly and somewhat surprisingly asked me to check and edit it. Frankly I think he was just being nice. A chap called Hinkley headed one part of the reorganised outfit and I was involved in the Departmental contribution to the early attempts to break the sound barrier. Much has been recorded about the UK anxiety regarding this programme. There was a feeling that the safety of pilots would be too much at risk if full-scale trials were conducted. The decision was to investigate the sonic barrier by using radio controlled models which would fly out from Cornwall into the Atlantic Ocean. I recall that they were to be launched from Mosquito aircraft.

I was requested to design and build a small transponder to fit into the models so that they could be tracked with ease. I made a unit the size of a double thickness chocolate slab about 8" x 4". Doing this with thermionic valves was very tricky. A lot of screening and earthing was necessary to stop unwanted self-oscillation, yet retaining adequate sensitivity. It worked quite well in the end, but it wasn't used, in fact, the programme folded and full scale flying recommenced.

A not to be forgotten aspect of the model programme took me to the Scilly Isles. A fair sized team from the Department under the famous Popham, was involved in setting up stations to monitor the model's progress. It was decided that aerials would be mounted on the Bishop Rock lighthouse. Someone would have to go there and decide where and how they were to be mounted and to measure the shape of the roof especially the weathercock. I wondered why I had been nominated for a flight to St Mary's in one of the Transport Flight DH Dominie (the military Dragon Rapide). I was soon to find out.

The Scilly Isles flying to and from Farnborough and the job itself occurred in June 1947. I spent my birthday on the island of Bryher when we saw a large school of porpoises in the harbour. An idiot shot at one once with an airgun and was made aware of our disgust. One of the team was an old school friend, Henry Hill. Actually Henry's birthday was also 15th June, the same as mine

The pilot who usually flew the Dominie was Flt. Lt. later Squadron Leader Hunt, a large and pleasant man. Landing on St. Mary's was not easy since it sloped up towards the middle and was a very small airfield. Popham was very energetic and had chaps doing a variety of tasks including digging a drain. At the end of the day he would suggest that we all go down into town to the Jack's Bar, a change from our collection of wartime huts. He would drive the Jeep at tremendous speed through the winding narrow lanes, his passengers hanging on for grim death and not a little scared. On the way back in the dark it was even more frightening, so we would look for excuses to stay in for the evening such

xvi - The Bishop Rock Lighthouse, as it was for the visit.

as lack of funds. Whereupon Pop would offer to buy the beer. There
was no way out. The jeep ride was nothing compared to the real job I
was given, fortunately this time accompanied by Pop. I had to measure
the weathercock on the Bishop Rock lighthouse. Flying was great but
climbing the outside of a slippery lighthouse in a high wind with nothing
but bare hands for safety was something else. In those days there was

79

no helicopter landing pad. I have illustrated the lighthouse as it was at the time. Only one person was able to take us out to the light and get us aboard, that was a Mr Jenkins in his launch. It cost HMG seven guineas, a lot of money in the late forties.

We went out in a fairly choppy sea and as we rounded the light I was amazed to see a keeper appear about one third of the way up the building at the front door. He looked very small as he climbed down an iron rung ladder to a platform, which had no safety rail. After much manoeuvring a rope was passed out to the launch. To my amazement I thought it would be the familiar Breeches Buoy but it turned out to be nothing more than a loop in the rope. Pop and I in turn had to put a leg through the loop and hang on to the rope, going up backwards. We lurched up and down alarmingly until hands grabbed us and pulled us on to the ledge. It was very slippery. I looked down and could see a seal swimming round the rock. I'm sure it must have thought what fools! I had a bag of tools with me. The climb up the wet rungs was not good but getting off the top rung into the front door, a long tunnel-like entrance was worse. Upstairs we were greeted by some exceedingly hospitable keepers. They gave us a hot cup of tea and showed us the light and the structure we would have to climb onto. I put my feet on the support rung and the whole damn thing moved. I was told it floated on mercury. Incidentally I noticed that the lighthousemen were knitting as a pastime.

We got onto the outer platform of the light itself and climbed up to the roof. I marked places for the aerial installation on the platform then we attempted to measure the weathercock. Hanging onto Pop's sailor's bags to keep him from falling off, I clung to the structure while he measured with one hand and sketched with this other with the wind whipping around us. I have retained the actual sketch and that original is copied here. I chiselled my initials alongside the aerial position marks, telling Pop that they were to assist the installer because I for one would not be coming to do it again. We were told that the weather was getting worse and we must return to the launch.

Going down for me was worse than going up because I couldn't find the first rung while going out backwards. To think these chaps serving there did it all the time. I suppose one gets used to anything. When we got back we were pretty wet. Pop threw his trousers on a coal bucket to dry.

One evening we met a lady in Jack's Bar who had flown a Percival Gull or Proctor, I forget which, to St Mary's. She asked if she could follow us back up the coast in loose formation and Squadron Leader Hunt agreed. Our aircraft was loaded with a coil of rope, lots of butter, still on ration, and new potatoes, plus a chap who came aboard and immediately pulled his parachute. So we were even more cramped. We had to take parachutes even in the Dominie.

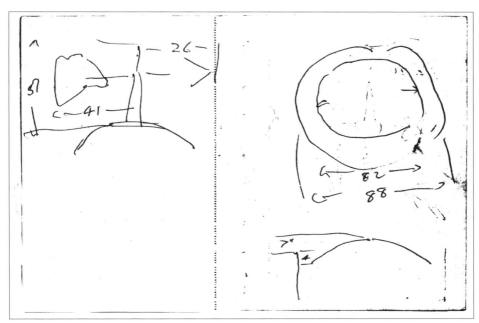

*xvii - **The drawing made by Popham of the Bishop Rock Weathercock.***

After take off, our lady pilot friend formatted with us on the port side. We flew low just above cliff top level over the sea on reaching the mainland. Imagine our concern when we saw her moving about at the controls and saw her wriggle out of her woollen cardigan while flying in formation! To add to our troubles our Aircraft Department passenger was airsick and he made a considerable mess. He was so ill that Hunt called for a doctor and ambulance at RAE immediately on landing. When we taxied to dispersal, a fitter had not seen our casualty disembark and he immediately assumed that I had made the mess.

The sonic barrier programme was linked with the use of an American centimetric mobile radar known as the 584. It was very complex and installed in a large trailer with an antenna dish on top. It was powered by an associated diesel trailer. Pop was the expert on this equipment too. This future boss of the Llambedr range in Wales enjoyed messing about in cars or any other practical equipment. His runabout at Farnborough was a Humber Snipe station wagon, but he could be found driving a lorry or anything else. He was unmarried until quite late after the war when I believe he was at Boscombe Down from where he retired. During the war he was great friends of the Gildersleeves who lived next door to my parents.

As a result of 584 interest I was sent down to Orfordness to meet two chaps operating the radar on the coast. I was not very happy there, living in an issue caravan out in the sticks. I learned practically nothing during my stay.

During the great freeze circa 1947, power was always being cut for lack of coal. RAE staff were concentrated in a few buildings. We were lodged temporarily in P161 Building which obtained electrical power from Pop's 584 generators. They were started by hand. By the time they were started you were warm enough to require little indoor heat for some time.

I was doing little flying at the time and started to look for some observer work to keep my hand in. I got to know a very good friend in Flt. Lt. Alan Marriott, an ex-Coastal Command pilot of the war years. I helped him do some of his work mostly flying in an Anson Mk I NK141, winding the 100 turns of the undercarriage for him as a fare. More about the Anson later. We also flew the Hudsons (two were in Coastal Command white and grey colours) a Fairey Firefly Mk I and Mu IV, also a Magister and a Lincoln. Alan gave me my first experience of a spin and recover in the Magister. The Anson was used among other things to monitor a Talking Beacon, the pet subject of Bernard Bryan, a future Deputy Mayor of Aldershot. A rotating aerial was coupled to a VHF transmitter and a rotary switch. The beam was reasonably narrow. As the aerial rotated the airborne receiver picked up voice transmissions on a tape coupled to the aerial. The pilot tuned to the beacon frequency then heard bearings given every 5° I recall. The loudest bearing was the bearing of the aircraft from the beacon. The beam width allowed two or three bearings either side of the correct bearing to be picked up. The system worked well and would have been an ideal alternative to the current Visual Omni Range (VOR) system. As with so many British inventions, it didn't get anywhere.

Alan Marriott, wife Rosie and small daughter, Barbara became great friends of ours. They came to tea when we were at Malmo (my parent's house in Leopold Avenue) and we even lived in their house for a week in Horsell (Woking) while they were on holiday. Alan took us all flying, including Renée, at Fairoaks in an Auster one fine afternoon.

For some reason the contact ended rather suddenly and although Henry Hill kept in touch, we didn't. I heard some years later that Alan was working for the CAA but that he had had a nervous breakdown. I still do not know if this was true or not.

Alan Marriott was not averse to letting his observers have a go at flying the Anson. He would climb out of the pilot's seat and go aft. Two or three of us including a navigator, F.O. Pittaway were doing this on 26th September 1946 with Pittaway in the seat when we developed a large oil leak in the port engine. A rapid reestablishment of the normal crew complementing took place and with the port engine throttled back and power applied to the starboard, height could not be maintained. We crept in to Farnborough on runway 18 with fire engines and ambulances riding behind.

Around that time in the late forties another navigator Johnnie Cole, a small fellow, was notable for his keenness to fly. On one occasion in a Wellington, not with me on board I hasten to add, the pilot asked Johnnie to check the master gyro which was suspended in a protecting cradle near the tail. The unit was suspended above an emergency exit which was a plywood diamond set in the geodetic structure of the fuselage. Johnnie had walked down the catwalk to the compass but was gone some time. The pilot asked another chap to go aft and see what he was up to. Johnnie was found halfway out of the aircraft having gone through the emergency hatch. He was hanging by his elbows and was swiftly dragged back into a safe and warm environment by strong pairs of hands.

Hinkley was fairly accommodating and he agreed to a particular trip from Farnborough around the UK including the north and northwestern highlands of Scotland in Lincoln aircraft RA 637 on 29th July 1947. I sat in the bomb aimers seat behind the glass house type windows right in front with a view downwards as well. I recall my impressions of the most remote mountains being similar to what I imagined the surface of the moon to look like.

Alan was instrumental in getting my brother Ivor his first flight. Ivor was on leave from Germany and he was allowed into the RAE in uniform (battledress). Kitted up with a parachute he flew with Alan as pilot with Ivor alongside him in a Flying Fortress, the US Boeing B17. They went from the parachute room in the usual Ford Station Wagon. On return Ivor picked up his parachute from the roof rack by the zip chord and pulled the chute. Red faces but it was laughed off.

Of course in later years Ivor joined the Territorial Army (TA) after de-mob. He was attached to an Air Observation Squadron and flew in Auster aircraft, usually with the Scots office, Bob Smith, a well-known member eventually of the Guild of Air Pilots and Air Navigators. Ivor in time got his PPL and flew an Auster many times from Booker (High Wycombe) airfield. He also flew a Currie Wot tiny single seat biplane and Piper Colt, the latter from White Waltham.

A most interesting trip with Alan was my first experience of flying in a helicopter Hoverfly I KL710 on 23rd June 1949. It was a Sikorsky R2, one of the first types to see service anywhere. During the trip we thought it would be a good idea to go over to the National Gas Turbine Establishment at the Old Site to see Renée, she was head of their Registry. We approached to within a few yards from her office window and hovered there. The window opened and Renée waved to us , a great thrill. Imagine such a trip being allowed in the 21st Century.

I had my chance to fly, or part fly, one of the Dominies, Alan got partly out of his cockpit to let me lean over and control it. My logbooks are the best record to ensure that chronological order is kept in this narrative.

Towards the end of the 1940s I was flying around quite a bit in the Dominies but had decided to get leave one half day each week to study for my BSc at Birkbeck College, University of London. I also was allowed off a bit early in the afternoon on other days and had some travel help in the form of a season ticket. To achieve a special physics degree, I had to take a four year course. It was killing work. No holidays, working Saturday mornings and homework on Sundays. The worst year required 5 nights getting home by train via Ash Vale and Frimley, leaving Waterloo at about 9.40 pm. The steam train to Farnborough had gone at 20.54. So I had to catch the electric train round the houses. God knows how I kept it up. Renée was a brick. She would greet me with a brandy and milk at about 20 to midnight, feed me and I would stagger off to bed. Up early next morning to work.

Keeping visitors, including relatives, away from me while I studied upstairs was of inestimable value. We did without holidays, without trips to the pictures or anything else until on one occasion I was so tired and fed up with work I threw the books at the wall. She picked them up and told me to carry on. She deserved the fruits of it all. Renée and I were engaged on 2nd June 1944, four days before D Day. We went to London and bought the engagement ring, a crossover two diamond in claws gold ring called Peek A-Boo. We came home and met Ivor at the top of Empress Avenue, full of enthusiasm, but deflated somewhat when he said he had guessed what we had to tell him. We were married in the Old Parish Church, Farnborough on 14th July 1945 between VE and VJ days. As I sat writing this on the terrace of the Campio Beach Hotel in Crete, overlooking the bay at Aghia Pelaghia on a warm evening on Sunday 23rd October 1988 with Renée sitting beside me, I thought of all the things that have happened since then. A visit to the British War Graves Cemetery brought the past sharply back into focus.

We had lived with my parents in one room for five and a half years having failed to find a home of our own. It was not easy for any of us despite the generosity of Dad and my Mum and Renée experiencing a difference in temperament and the generation gap. In 1950 we eventually acquired land in Revelstoke Avenue to build Beverley Fair. The Empress Estate on which it is situated originally belonged to the Empress Eugenie, wife of Napoleon III. We had the house designed by Col.Austin Barton of Camberley and it was ready for us to move in on 15 December 1950, our own home at last. We did it all on Renée's low pay and my AEO salary of some £450 per annum. Dad gave us a small loan and acted as guarantor and also helped us to clear dense undergrowth and trees to allow building to start. The whole garden took seven years to complete.

In 1947 it was decided that the Civil Service should be put on a proper peacetime footing. The Scientific Service personnel had to enter for selection by the Civil Service Commission and new grades were to be created, I applied as an Assistant Experimental Officer (AEO) and was duly boarded and to my delight, I passed. Subject to a medical, taken by Dr Hill, our old GP in Aldershot, I was established.

Soon after this I was transferred to G1 again, this time under a PSO John Todd, a Welshman with one eye – a golfer who was in digs with his wife and son next door to my parents. They lived with Dulcie Bairstow, wife of Major Bairstow, Royal Tank Regiment whose son Gordon, a very nice boy, was in the same Regiment and died of wounds in the North African fighting.

I had not relished the transfer and found myself part of an augmented team to develop a navigation system called the Post Office Position Indicator – or POPI. Yet another great effort which came to nought. However, it taught me a lot, particularly the technical expertise passed on to me by Johnny Ashton, an Experimental Officer who was promoted to Senior Experimental Officer soon after I joined. Johnny had considerable talents in the electronics field. He designed transformers and circuits. He gave me a lot of encouragement in obtaining my degree. He smoked a lot and was very conscientious. He was married but they had no children and lived in Victoria Road, Cove. He had likes and dislikes – he especially disliked one PSO he later worked for. We were technical colleagues for some time later and he was chosen to head up a part of the Red Shrimp V Bomber jamming teams but had heart trouble and died in harness one morning in P161 Building.

POPI was a fairly complex low frequency beacon using a phase system of bearing measurement from a ground transmitter with a complex aerial array. An experimental transmitter was positioned on an old wartime airfield at Earl's Colne near Colchester. It had been an American fighter base alongside another similar airfield at Boxted. The POPI team included Donald Collyer, later to go to Fort Halstead, Vin Lavelle, retired who lived near us in Farnborough, Bill Langrish and Henry Hill, old school friends from the Grammar School.

Much laboratory time was spent in providing precision potentiometers wound by a firm called Johnson Mathey. A wartime rival system worked on by Albert Brown in P160 Building and Henry was called Consol. Bearing was provided over very long range by a system of dots and dashes. The observer counted them and referred to a chart. He then knew his bearing from the station. Consol was sited at Bushmills in Ireland and had actually been used by both sides during the war.

I had occasion to go to Earl's Colne and stay at a hotel in Marks Tay on the A12. The manager and his wife knew Albert and Henry well. There were few guests and we enjoyed a chat with the manager in the evening over a drink. A very amusing story he told us concerned a honeymoon couple. They arrived and during dinner it was evident that the girl was very shy. They went off to bed on their wedding night after dinner but during the night both the manager and his wife heard a loud bang coming from the honeymoon couple's room. Next morning only the chap came down to breakfast, there was no sign of the bride. After breakfast the groom asked the manager somewhat nervously if he would go up to the bedroom with him since he wanted to show him something. On entering the two lovebirds stood anxiously awaiting a reaction. The sight that greeted their host was the complete washbasin, detached from the wall, face down on the floor with the water pipes bent over in an arc still connected to the taps. Naturally it was considered unwise to enquire how the catastrophe had occurred. Financial compensation for damage was the only topic of discussion. It did not stop us all wondering just how it had all happened or how injury was averted.

The late 1940s saw the Preliminary International Civil Air Organisation (PICAO), the predecessor of the International Civil Air Organisation, sending a team of experts from many countries to the UK for a demonstration of radio and radio navigation aids for civil aircraft. The aids were derivatives of wartime devices such as Decca, Consol, SCS51, later to become ILS, the instrument landing system, VHF communications, the talking beacon and maybe others which escape my memory. Two aircraft were fitted with all of these systems which were arranged to have instrument displays available for viewing by the delegates. The two aircraft York MW272 and York MW313 were in natural metal colour. Two observers were selected, myself and 'Rog' Rogers to be the demonstrators. We had intercommunication circuits to allow us to talk to either the delegates or pilot or both. After much practice we started the flying, becoming quite adept at navigating and pattering our progress around a cross country circuit using each aid in turn and rounding the flight off with a pattered instrument approach. Many flights were required and I was delighted to achieve 55 hours airborne time on one month alone.

Flying in the Yorks test flights started on 29th August, on 2nd September 1946 in MW272 with Flt Lt. 'Sailor' Parker on the second sortie and Flt. Lt. 'Tich' Taylor on the first; trips were to High Wycombe and to Avonmouth respectively testing Decca.

Tich had been a member of the Pathfinder Force during the War and had flown Mosquitoes during the release of Denmark from German occupation. He came to Radio Flight during the War as a Flight Lieutenant and he brought many captured German aircraft back to this country at the end of hostilities, mainly flying a French Siebel aircraft for ferrying purposes; the aircraft had been part of the Luftwaffe. Tich left the RAF but took the unusual step of becoming a civilian test pilot at RAE. I kept up some flying between August 1945 and the PICAO project by persuading pilots I knew to let me fly with them.

By 5th September 1946 I was flying with Alan Marriott, 'Sailor' and 'Tich', mostly in MW313. The real demonstrations began on 11th September with 'Tich'. Each demonstration involved 1½ hours of flying. The last demonstration was on 27th September.

During the PICAO flying I accompanied Alan in the Anson on Condor flying – Condor being a navigation aid. One comment in my logbook on 23rd September states 'dropped message at Walbury Hotel'! Flying on the Talking Beacon – the pride and joy of Bernard Bryan, took me with Sailor and Alan in Beaufighter RD388 in December 1946.

xviii - Avro York MW272.

1947 began with a flight in Lancaster III EE 187 with Sailor Parker observing Decca including a height check on 2nd January. Between January and May I was working in the 70 Building laboratory as mentioned earlier, building the very small transponder.

In May and June 1947 I was allowed out to fly with Alan in a Firefly I (PP435), Oxford (LX305) and Dominie (X7375). By 12th June 1947 I started flying in the Dominie with Flt. Lt. Hunt to St Mary's in the Scilly Isles, it took 2 hours.

Alan gave me the opportunity in the summer of 1948 to fly with him to assist in a variety of programmes involving different aircraft types such as Wellington MlX RP589 (aerial VHF trials) in which he let me have some dual flying. A radiator temperature test on 2000 ft in a Firefly Mk IV (TW6370) was interesting, also York MW272 and Magister P2388 on 2nd July when we did some dual and aerobatics when I experienced my first spin on that flight.

In 1949 John Todd decided that a series of measurements should be made to examine the long range potential of POPI since it was a low frequency aid to navigation. I was joined by Henry Hill to make up a two-man team and to sail on board a Royal Navy frigate, (HMS Sheerwater?) attached to Admiralty Signals and Radar Establishment (ASRE) at Portsmouth. Monitoring gear was put aboard and we set sail for Denmark via the Kiel Canal and Nordhaven. I had not been abroad before although I had sailed in the Channel with the Belgian Commandos during the war and had flown over the Channel Islands. I was staggered by the bomb damage in Germany. The accuracy of some of it was remarkable. Although some years had passed since VE day, our arrival at Nordhaven was to be somewhat amusing, although a lasting impression was the sight of the remains of the Third Reich navy upside down in the harbour.

The amusement was caused by the performance of the crew as we secured alongside. I was informed that the Navy do not tie up to anything, they secure alongside. Incidentally we learned a lot of nautical phrases during the exercise and we were instructed to wear a hat so that we could raise it as we boarded in response to the salute by the officer of the watch. An admiral and his entourage were waiting for the arrival of the ship and Henry and I were instructed to get below because were not in the the the 'rig of the day'. The young subaltern with telescope under his arm stood smartly on the foredeck with a young seaman at the bow holding a rope. On command he threw the rope, or is it a sheet, to the man waiting for it on the quay. He did not throw it hard enough and forgot to hold on to the boat end and the whole rope fell into the water. Number One and others went mad and all in front of the important gathering on the shore. We watched all this through a scupper – the naval version of a porthole.

We did our scientific recording of signal strength from the station at Boreham during the night, to measure the ionospheric causes of error in the PPOI system. Only one bearing was possible from each station, and with hindsight, the system was only a slight advance upon the German Condor system and our version of it in the UK or upon Loran and perhaps Decca.

After our arrival in Nordhaven the crew or most of them were given leave to go ashore one evening. Henry and I did not have the appropriate papers to let us enter Germany which was still under strict military administration. We were invited to enjoy the contents of the bar making a note on slips of any drinks we took; the cost was only a few pence each! After sampling several bottles we could not find the slips of paper.

Two sailors had been confined below for some misdemeanour but were allowed upon deck for exercise and fresh air while the bulk of the crew were ashore. Their guard had not noticed the two defaulters talking to two ladies of the night calling to them from the quay. Both lads suddenly jumped over the rail and ran into the darkness with the girls!. By the time the guards caught up with them in the maze of coal heaps etc it was too late. They were arrested again and put below. During our trip in the Baltic Sea towards Copenhagen, I witnessed the amazing spectacle of the Naval version of an orderly room scene. Number One, who was second in command on board, stood in the space of a normal house pantry, with a tall narrow lectern type desk in front of him. With much shouting and banging of feet, the two naughty chaps were marched in one by one. After much exclamation of displeasure by the officer, mostly in the vernacular, both chaps were sentenced to be put in cells aboard HMS Sheffield which would be at Copenhagen upon our arrival as the mother ship for a flotilla of submarines visiting the city. I pondered that the Army did at least have more room to move in the Orderly Room where defaulters were marched in for the C.O. to deal with. One bit of excitement in the Baltic was the flap caused when the watch saw a mine nearby which was eventually identified as an empty oil drum.

Copenhagen proved to be a most wonderful place to visit. Despite the occupation during the war, the fact that the British had freed the Danes made us very popular. The sight of electric signs in the streets was amazing since restrictions in the UK at the time did not allow such luxury. The amount and variety of food was the greatest attraction. The meagre rations at home and the dreadful restaurant menus and service were not much better than during the war. In Copenhagen however, there was so much food, variety and delightful service that we thought it a touch of heaven. A long quiet meal in Gronegan's will never be forgotten, especially the chicken and mushroom soup.

Henry and I returned with our results to England by civil transport, rail and ship via Ebsjerg. The equipment stayed on board the frigate. Unfortunately the sea was very rough indeed and so much so that the propellers of the ferry would lift clean out of the water as huge waves battered us. Henry was very poorly and stayed in his bunk the whole time. We were nearly half a day late on arrival in Harwich.

I briefed Henry on the results and he took them into RAE to present to the boss. I had advised the latter that I would be going straight off on leave, potato picking at Burton Bradstock in Dorset where Renée was waiting for me. The working holiday was fun but John Todd was not amused and informed me on my return that I should have gone into RAE myself and that Henry reporting the results of the tests was not enough. I thought his remarks were unjust and decided that life would have more promise in a section where there was more interesting work and flying activity.

As stated earlier, in 1947 I had applied to the Civil Service Commission for acceptance in an established capacity as an Assistant Experimental Office during the reorganisation of the Scientific Civil Service after the war. I was successful so subsequently decided to study for more qualifications and better things.

I approached my Division leader with the suggestion that it would be a good career move if I joined the Caradoc Williams Group which was very much concerned with a variety of navigational aids such as Decca, Instrument Landing System (ILS) and Automatic Direction Finder (ADF). My request was granted and I was summoned into the presence of Caradoc, a man with great insight and integrity but a strict disciplinarian and with a Welsh dedication to his Christian faith and the Congregational Church.

I came to know Caradoc and his family very well over a period of years, in fact he did an enormous amount for my career. The initial interview was not very promising however, since he said he had heard that I had 'chucked my weight about'. I wonder who had spread that story since I had been pushed around by a large number of people ever since joining the Establishment. However, over the six years that I stayed in his group, I must have changed his view because he arranged my interview and board eventually for a double promotion. I was also promoted during that time to Experimental Officer, so that six years changed things from EO to Senior Scientific Officer, a rather rare change.

Caradoc was all in favour of my degree course and he was very pleased when I graduated. He dissuaded me from going for my MSc since he rightly considered that I didn't need more to get on with my career. As mentioned earlier I had travelled to London three or four evenings per week and Saturday mornings. I also did Wednesday afternoons sometimes. The RAE paid my fare but after a day's work, often flying, then travel, lectures and return by about midnight, took its toll. At one time I thought I had an ulcer but it was only an indication that rest was needed. Weekends were all spent studying. Renée did valiant work keeping relatives at bay while I studied upstairs. After Part One we took a holiday at the Talbooth on the River Stour in Constable Country. We travelled by train and bicycle. It was a wonderful place to relax. The hotel is very upmarket now, in fact we were the last guests before the old ladies who ran it then sold up. Drifting along the river in a boat watching the kingfishers was in the words of Ned Larkin in the Darling Buds of May, 'perfick'.

I began my work with Caradoc by being placed in the care of his second in command, a Senior Scientific Officer (SSO) at the time, called Albert Brown, a very able and charming man who, after being made Principal Scientific Officer (PSO), left to occupy a senior civil aviation post in New Zealand. Albert introduced me to the state of the art at the time in Radio Direction Finding and the Automatic Direction Finder, ADF, so well known now to all pilots. The interest was to investigate the propagational errors introduced by ionospheric effects of reflection upon phase and signal amplitude at various distances by night and day. A new window on the world was opened. I had an ex British Airways Viking VW227 at my disposal. As an AEO the freedom to fly abroad with a full aircrew operating to my wishes was tremendous. We used a GEC airborne equipment and tested errors by comparison with Decca, Gee and other aids, long reports were prepared and after standard range tests we began a series of flights to measure errors at night at various speeds relative to a ground beacon. An RAF Flight Lieutenant, Eric Cropper joined me. He had experienced a hard war as a Bomber Command navigator in Lancasters. We became great family friends and still keep in touch after 50 years. He became a Group Captain before he retired.

Albert came up with the splendid idea of checking the effect by flying the Viking firstly on a straight path which believe it or not took me to

Copenhagen again. For various reasons my propagation work took me some fourteen times to that lovely city. The constant radius zero effective speed was achieved by flight along the circumference of circle centred on broadcast transmitters in England such as Droitwich and Brookmans Park. The flight paths were over the north sea. Half speed was achieved by flying a logarithmic spiral track which took some doing on behalf of the aircrew. They did a wonderful job and well deserved their relaxation in and around our hotel, the Cosmopolite, situated in Kongens Nytof. It is now a block of offices or was the last time I went to Copenhagen years later. Flights were conducted at night and bearing errors were measured by coupling the DF loop to a pen recorder. Results proved very interesting since at night the mix of ground and sky waves produced sinusoidal swings about the true bearing. The amplitude was large and frequency of about one wavelength every few minutes at the 200kHz end of the ADF band, whereas at medium frequency the intervals decreased but the amplitude was erratic. At the high frequency end of the band the variations were rapid but at lower amplitude and more predictable. We measured coastline refraction and all of the effects to which ADF, or the Radio Compass as it was known, were prone. Today pilots use ADF a lot and I have taught many student pilots to use it, but my early experiences made a lasting impression of distrust of the system for its use in really poor weather or at night. The cone of silence over the beacon was checked and all of this data published in the largest technical report that I had published up to that time.

The pen recorder used a rolling paper chart. A pen, with a constant reservoir of black ink, indicated the bearing errors. It was a vital piece of kit. The little pen head had to be screwed on to the moving arm. It often blocked and needed cleaning. One night over the North Sea, I dropped the head on the aircraft floor. It was smaller than that the size of a pea. I groped around on the floor looking for it, not saying a word as the aircraft ploughed on in flight at 180 knots. I found it eventually and no one asked later why there was a long gap in the results.

A very interesting range test took us to Istres in Southern France and then on to Rome. Gerry Chandler was the pilot and I have a photograph of him I took in the air as he flew us on the Rome leg. The navigator helping me as part of Caradoc's group was Flt. Lt. Paddy Carson. He later rose to Group Captain. An amazing aspect of the trip was that it coincided with a visit the Empire Test Pilots School was making to an aircraft carrier of the US Navy moored in Naples harbour. A Dakota was arranged to fly the EPTS students to Naples but they had more visitors than the Dakota would hold. They asked me if I could take the surplus in our Viking. I agreed. Imagine my indignation when they told me that had more passengers than expected and could my team and myself stay behind! I was pretty firm in explaining that they were coming aboard my aircraft not me aboard theirs. On the way one of them amused himself by flying the Viking and pitching it up and down to amuse his colleagues, but not me as we were trying to get some serious daylight data down the back. We managed homing as far as the coast on the Mediterranean. To measure the value of the signal strength the rate of rotation of the loop aerial was measured in seconds as it homed onto the correct bearing from a deliberate and pre-determined deflection.

Istres was still in its damaged wartime state. Norman Watson, the Viking navigator from Radio Flight was walking to our hotel in the evening after our arrival. Near the station he saw an old lady struggling with a large heavy suitcase. A true Scottish gentleman, Norman went to help and, not speaking much French just took the suitcase from the lady who screamed thinking that he was stealing it.

Our landing on a hot August weekend in Naples enabled us to drop the ETPS pilots and we saw their carrier in the misty heat with Vesuvius as a backdrop. We found two Italian ground crew and a petrol electric set to start the Viking. The PE set would not start and the two Italians pulled and pulled on the starter cord until they were nearly exhausted in the heat. Gerry said "oh well, let's see if she will start on internals" and she did! The Italians looked most dejected.

We arrived in Rome and were put into the Hotel Mediterranie. Paddy Carson and I shared a room. It was a very hot afternoon and a cold bath was an urgent need. I chose first go and was surprised to see how well appointed was the bathroom. I managed to get the water flowing but could not find how to stop it running away. A small sliding trap door was clearing the device that closed the drain, I operated every control in sight. The water did not stop running away but I looked round to find to my embarrassment that a young Italian maid was standing behind me. I had rung the bell in my efforts to fill the bath. Some hand waving and she showed me the right control then discreetly retired. When I told the chaps in the bar about the episode, they thought an immediate bath would be in order for them but settled for a cool drink instead.

While in Rome we attended the Caracala Baths and heard Tito Gobi singing in Rigaletto. We decided to walk back to the hotel but Paddy wanted to ride. He overtook us in style riding in an open horse drawn carriage.

Much of the Decca propagation measurements flying was done in York MW272, one of the aircraft that had been used for the PICAO demonstrations. Many hours of night flying out to the Bay of Biscay and back compiled a wealth of data for Caradoc's comprehensive report on the subject. We measured vertically and horizontally polarised signals from specially designed aerials fitted to the York. Caradoc flew frequently on these flights. On one occasion when results were very poor he had a suspicion that I had not connected the aerial to the feeder. It was installed over the false ceiling in the York and he made me climb up to investigate, a bit unnerving in flight on a dark night. Night flying in the York caused me some alarm when I saw all the sparks emitted from the exhausts of the Merlin engines. Six hours with those four engines and propellers near one were very tiring. Squadron Leader, later Air Vice Marshall Giddings on a daylight trip feathered three of the four engines. The port outer kept us up although descending; it was very quiet then. Fortunately they all started OK. On take-off on one occasions, I noticed a lot of fluid flowing from the port inner. It proved to be water but I kept the fact to myself remembering how other pilots had told me not to interfere. He scolded me for not attracting his attention. I learned another lesson, that is, you seldom win.

One night when I was not on board the York, the door came open miles out to sea. The crew could not shut it and had to contend with tying a rope to the handle to prevent a catastrophe; they endured extreme cold for the rest of the flight.

We still flew in the Viking. An evening trip with another well-known pilot caused me to be bold enough to ask him if he really needed full flap for take-off. A rapid raising of flaps ensued. The incident did not improve the day for him since he had joined me later at the aircraft having mistakenly got into the wrong Viking and only realised his initial error when I didn't turn up.

A graduate from Cambridge, Sir Claud Alexander came to P160 Building and joined us on the top floor laboratory to pursue some of his own propagational research on behalf of the university. He used the York and sometimes a Lancaster for his recordings. Several interesting facets of his work stick in the memory, but probably the most telling was the car accident. I was still working hard at Birbeck in the evenings and although I had a perfectly good railway season ticket, I accepted a lift from Claud one winter's evening. We drove off in his Austin Devon but along the A3 at Ripley a lorry backed out of a side road into our path and we hit it fair and square writing off the Devon and nearly doing the same for both of us. I collapsed after extricating myself with head and knees hurting like mad. We were both kept in hospital overnight, my hand hit the windscreen, no seatbelts in those days, and Claud hit the steering wheel with his chest. I called Renée from the X Ray table and frightened her unfortunately. She came to see me – her Dad drove and so did Lady Alexander, Claud's mother. I was off work for about six weeks and was surprised at home by a visit from both Caradoc and Albert, and was very pleased that they should care. I received no compensation, Claud was broke. The only witness died before we could take any legal action and the whole thing was forgotten. I had not known that Claud had eyesight trouble. Our flights to and from Copenhagen continued over a period of months in both the Viking and the York. Claud accompanied us in the York. He left his raincoat on the peg in the public cloakroom at the Cosmopolite on one occasion and thought he had lost it. On return 6 weeks later it was still hanging on the peg. The Danes were an honest crowd of people.

On another trip we had permission to take the wife of an American General back to the UK from Copenhagen (Kastrup Airport). She had been rescued from Mont Blanc by a Fiesler Storch or a Piper Cub on skis which landed on the snow capped mountainside to pick up the crew and passengers of an aircraft which had crashed on the mountain. She sat in the back of the York but was not on intercom like the rest of us. Tich Taylor was Captain of the aircraft with Tiffy Adshead engineer and a navigator and radio operator completed the crew. Claud had most of his valve component birds nest of a circuit on a breadboard on the floor of the aircraft. I was monitoring more impressive and well engineered equipment further forward. As we flew at night over the North Sea with thunderstorm activity some miles to the south there was an almighty bang as the aircraft was struck by lightning. Claud switched off his gear thinking it had blown up since, contrary to all scientific theory, a blue flash had danced along the metal floor. A yell from the front indicated that Tich had been temporarily blinded by the flash and although controlling the aircraft manually could not see his instrument panel. Tiffy complained of a sudden pain in his knee and the radio operator had a hurt face because his aerial J switch had blown up in front of him. For a while frantic shouting saturated the intercom. Afterwards the General's wife, who was not party to all of the alarm on the intercom said "Gee you boys were brave, it was just like the other one started". Little did she know how frightened the 'brave' boys were.

Actually the lightning had knocked off the trailing aerial, and had welded all other aerials to the fuselage. We continued without radio communication and decided to make an emergency landing at Lyneham. An Aldis light was used from the ground to clear us for landing. As dawn broke we elected to return to Farnborough but Lyneham ATC denied permission stating that the York was unserviceable. Tich ignored all that, told us to get aboard and he took off. Nothing more was said; things were different in those days.

Tiffy Adshead enjoyed his trips to the Cosmopolite but spent most of his time during daylight rest periods playing poker dice at the bar with anyone who would join him. At meal times, he would order a beer and ham and eggs at the bar. He would come out for dinner in the evening. I overhead him back at RAE discussing overseas trips with someone telling the listener of the beauty of Copenhagen. He said that Copenhagen was a good place to go if you knew where to go when you were there!

The Viking flights produced many memorable incidents. On one memorable occasion, Johnny Kent, the famous Battle of Britain pilot, captained the aircraft. 'Put Another Nickel In' was a juke box No. 1 song at the time. I recall the crew singing it together on the stage of a night club by popular request (in uniform!).

A long daylight flight home in the Viking caused Norman Watson the navigator and myself on one of the trips to decide upon an early night.

We shared a room in the Cosmopolite and thought we would just have a look at the permanent fairground at Klampenborg (a short train journey) and then a quick beer and bed. While at the fair I had the unnecessary experience of being chased by a flock of geese. While we had a quick drink around the corner from the hotel, an American USAF officer asked us if we would join him and his wife. A long evening resulted since a floor show started. The northern summer day started at 3 am and as Norman and I got ready for bed, Norman decided to visit the gents down the corridor. He was gone a very long time but returned eventually looking very unhappy. He told me that he found three doors, one marked Damen, one marked Herren and one marked Brandetrap. Mistakenly he went through one which latched behind him. He went up and down the fire escape in pyjamas and slippers but could not get back inside. He had to descend to the ground into a courtyard, go out into the street and enter the hotel by the front entrance past a surprised commissionaire. On arrival in our bedroom, he said "and I still have not done what I set out to do!"

Eric Cropper and I did a lot of work upon Automatic Direction Finding propagation by making measurements on the ground as well as in the air. We worked a lot at night in a sort of windmill type of tower in the field alongside the Cove Wireless Station. It was black on the outside and inside it seemed to be the collecting point for most of the bluebottles in the world. These large flies were everywhere when we arrived. The experiment complemented those in the Viking trials. The flights abroad gave us high speed measurements and the Cove measurements gave us zero speed. In between we flew the logarithmic spiral track over the North Sea. That gave us an equivalent slow speed radial from the transmitting stations while the aircraft was actually flying at cruising speed. We also did some work on the top of the hill on the south side of the airfield overlooking the field itself. Measurements during warm summer days were very pleasant as compared with the confines of the Cove tower at night. I eventually recorded all the findings in a comprehensive report which had a fairly wide circulation. I was pleased with it since the results not only supported the findings of earlier work by Busignes but added much material to them.

The most rewarding aspect of the work was when the Deputy Head of Radio Department, Philip Edwards took me, a mere Assistant Experimental Officer, to the Cabinet Offices to present the ADF results to a NATO committee in London, emphasising aspects relevant to military operations.

Flt. Lt. Eric Cropper, a wartime Bomber Command Navigator with many missions under his belt, left us to further his career, eventually achieving Group Captain – an unusual success for a navigator. Joan and Eric became firm friends and they were very excited when we moved into the newly built home of Beverley Fair on 15th December 1950. They retired to North Yorkshire and keep in touch at Christmas.

One of Eric's wartime missions was the bombing of Caen in Normandy after D Day. It was a remarkable coincidence that my brother Ivor was in the 11th Armoured Division waiting to attack the Germans as soon as the bombing ceased. Apparently the ground heaved as they waited in the tanks to attack and as the massive raid was in progress.

Eric's aircraft was damaged when a bomb from a higher aircraft fell onto the rear turret of his Lancaster. The rear gunner was killed and the pilot crash landed at Tangmere, I believe. Eric said that the Lancaster was bulldozed off the runway into a dump of crashed aircraft while the remaining crew sought succour in the bottom of a glass.

Eric was replaced on the Caradoc Williams team by Ted Bullock. Ted was a Spec. N. (Specialist Navigator) coming to us with much experience from Shawbury where he instructed on such systems as Gee. He was originally a peace time Cranwell apprentice, affectionately known as 'brats'. He told many amusing stories about his time at Cranwell and subsequently. A real song and dance man Ted's arrival coincided with my introduction to the latest navigational aid of the 1950s viz TACAN or Tactical Air Navigation. It was a distance/bearing system, devised originally by the United States and operating in the 950-1350 MHz frequency band or thereabouts. Our particular role was to guide industry in the production of a British version and to test the whole system prior to introducing it to the RAF. A simple display meter was able to provide the distance and bearing (RO) of a ground beacon. I was the airborne system project office and Dave Southern looked after the ground transmitter receiver known as URN-3. The transmitter was positioned on the hill which is now the SBAC site and the tower which supported the aerials still stands there at the time of writing some 50 years later.

I was also joined by an RAF Flight Sergeant who was detailed to prepare the Servicing Manuals for the airborne equipment. Tacan is still in service today and has been used for years in RAF fighter aircraft.

We welcomed the arrival of two Varsity aircraft in which to complete our airborne trials viz VL674 and VL679. VL679 was still flying at Farnborough for many years and during the intervening years had been a workhorse for much of the night vision research such as infra-red. Surely it was one of the longest serving of our test aircraft and the only Varsity left airworthy.

A photograph of VL674 is shown in the illustrations. It includes the team and illustrates both Tacan and the test apparatus. The aircraft were modified to have all observers sitting with backs to the direction of flight on strong benches arranged with safety in mind. This RAE design gave us a lot of trouble. Stressed for a crash landing the structure constricted our legs and movement. We still carried parachutes and although the system could stand a crash, we could not evacuate quickly because of all the struts and wooden cross bracing under the tables.

***xix - F.S.S. and the Tacan Team in Varsity VL674, 1956.
(Crown Copyright MoD)***

The airborne equipment was very complex and the early versions of course used valve type components and the total bulk and weight, not to mention power consumption, was high. My contacts with industry were very much enhanced by the Tacan project and the display components gave me my first contact with Smith's Instruments at Cheltenham (Bishops Cleeve).

I learned another lesson while working on Tacan, such as thinking about speaking diplomatically. I was required at a Tacan progress meeting at MOD Castlewood House in London. Seated at a long conference table were two rows of RAF officers. The Chairman at one end was Air Commodore Bell. I was at the other end. After some preliminaries the Chairman asked, "Mr Stringer, what is holding up the development programme of airborne Tacan?" I replied, "Mr Chairman, this meeting is holding up progress!" He was not at all pleased, I have not done that again, even if it was true.

At the time of our Tacan work Caradoc suggested that I should devise a means of assisting fighter aircraft to intercept a formation of bombers using the 'broadcast control' method. Transistors had not come along so I had to devise something which would make a useful addition to Tacan.

The broadcast control technique differed from the wartime individual radar interception using GCI and AI systems. A GCI station would identify a hostile formation and periodically broadcast on Ultra High Frequency

(UHF) the position, height, direction and speed of the bombers. Each fighter formation would then perform a visual interception with the aid of its own navigational equipment.

I solved the problem with the aid of a very simple design. A mu-metal plate was arranged with rollers top and bottom to allow a sheet with a grid of distance bearings and Georef. rectangular position coordinates drawn over a map of the operational area. Three small magnets were placed on the map, one of the fighter's Tacan position, one on the reported bomber georef coordinate and one on the estimated interception point. Small arrows and a circular scale on two of the magnets were used to give heading of each aircraft formation. A simple ratio scale in the fighter cockpit gave the pilot the opportunity of estimating the interception point. It all sounds complicated but it was really very simple. Since updates were frequent, the accuracy proved to be very high.

We began airborne tests with a Devon using Decca instead of Tacan, and a Miles Marathon as the bomber. Since simulation was the name of the game initially the Marathon crew broadcast their position, heading, speed and height. It was most rewarding to have 100% success each time.

We then considered the introduction of the system to the Meteor Mk8 then in service with Fighter Command.

One of the most taxing problems was the provision of a suitable housing and bracket to take the equipment which eventually was nicknamed Freddy Stringer's 'Weegy Board'. During normal flight the board was stowed in a metal pocket. For operation it was withdrawn and two spigots on the board were lodged with spring ball bearings into holes in the bracket on the side of the fuselage. Surprisingly little cockpit instrumentation was obscured on the Meteor or later on the Venom.

In the autumn of 1955 several Meteor aircraft of No. 63 Squadron at Waterbeach were fitted with the system and it was tried in Exercise Momentum. Again it all worked fine and gave me the chance of flights in a Meteor 7 used to transport me home to Farnborough. I used to jam my suitcase between the two cockpits under the canopy.

Having completed the Waterbeach exercises where 63 and 56 Squadrons were involved, I departed to Wunsdorf in Germany where the boards were installed in Venom aircraft for use in identifying ground targets. It worked well but after all of the excitement the system was dropped in favour of a more complex device using several scales on a piece of wood or metal looking like a complicated pencil. It was devised by the Central Fighter Estabishment chaps at West Raynham. The reason given for dropping my system was that in the new Hunter aircraft about to come into service, the board obscured the generator warning light! As if the light could not be moved to an alternative position.

Our daughter Carol was born on 21st July 1954 and that produced a monumental celebration with Ted and his wife, Dot, also Norman Ruffle who was promoted at that time. I was then an Experimental Officer and rode back from the nursing home at Farley House calling at the Tumble Down Dick on my bike to buy a bottle of brandy to wet the baby's head at Ted's house in Cove. Norman later turned up with a bottle of whisky. We compromised with a Wandy (a mixture of whisky and brandy!). Ted thought it would be unsafe for me to ride home on my bike and we should take his car. The ride home in Ted's car was quite a performance. The journey was nearly concluded when we reached the narrow Prospect Road railway bridge. We stopped at the slight rise, (now the position of a traffic light) and Ted said, "You are a good shot, aim for it." So I shut an eye and steered through while Ted operated the gears. Not a technique encouraged today. I went back the next day to collect my bike.

During the period 1954 -56, Caradoc encouraged me to design new radio navigation aids with various military operations in mind. Not the least of these assumed a Malaysian jungle scenario. The designs were described in papers and I was given the chance of presenting them to senior RAF staff officers. They were great days. By that time my studies were complete and I obtained my degree from the Earl of Athlone, with Dad present with me in the Albert Hall. Renée couldn't come as she was expecting Carol at the time. It was a strange coincidence that the Guards Orchestra conductor was Major Fred Harris who had been bandmaster with the 2nd Battalion East Yorkshire Regiment in Catterick in 1930-34. We went to his dressing room after the ceremony to say hello and found him him, not in his Guards uniform but in his long johns.

There were occasions when I had the opportunity to fly on a variety of exercises. One such was in the Valetta used for ILS development. Henry Hill and I were going about our business when an engine failed. The pilot instructed us to put our parachutes on and be ready to bale out. After standing by the door for some 15 minutes, he told us he thought he could get down all right and we had better return to our stations. We had used up a lot of adrenaline in the process.

In the 1950s, the new Viscount propeller driven turbo engine aircraft had appeared. This was a significant step forward in passenger aircraft design. The prototype G-AHRF required tests upon new type suppressed aerials. Day and night tests were flown by a Boscombe Down aircrew from Wisley airfield. Reg Knight, an ex RAF officer with a large handlebar moustache, was captain most of the time. I was the boffin with all of my recording gear installed. Reg met a party of us walking in Copenhagen. He said, "A Dane stopped me just now and spoke to me in English. I wonder how he knew I was English," He was dressed in a blazer and flannels with RAF tie and a large badge of office on his face – fighter command whiskers!

The airfield continued to provide excitement. A pall of smoke seen out of the lab window was caused by a Vampire having engine failure, landing wheels up at the end of 07 runway and proceeding on the ground through South Gate into the road near the RAE mess. It caught fire but the duty policeman on the gate got the pilot out and was later given a medal for his bravery. We also watched from the York, an aircraft which had gone in out in the Fox Hills area.

The Navigation Group Laboratory was on the top floor of P160 Building. The railway outside the building was regularly in use bringing coal to the power station and stores along the front of ˙F1E hangar. Towards the end of my time with the Group, interest was shown in highly stable Caesium oscillators for the control of radio transmissions for navigation purposes. Decca and other systems were involved. I was selected to give a broadcast talk on BBC3 on the subject. My worry during the presentation was that the BBC wanted everything explained in simple, almost puerile terms. Having felt that it was such a childish explanation of the technical advances, which would be used in future navigational systems, would cause derision among my colleagues, I was told by Mrs Hill, Secretary of the Head of Radio Department, that it was very technical! Dr Mc Petrie gave me much successful support in persuading the Ministry to let me keep the fee I received from the BBC which the headquarter staff wanted me to surrender to them.

Dr McPetrie took a keen interest in what was going on. He read reports very carefully. Once during Eric Cropper's time I let him have a draft of one of my reports or memoranda and he found a small error and asked for it to be corrected. We amended the text but the correction escaped the notice of the printers and the error remained. I well recall an irate McPetrie coming up the stairs of 160 Building to ask why his instruction had not been obeyed.

Ted and I would go for a drink at the Tower Hill Arms some evenings, he would telephone, and without preamble, would just say, "are you thirsty?" When I bought our first car, a Morris (1935) he got me back into the way of driving again. I had taken my licence and test in an Austin 12 or some such in about 1948. Although I had a licence I had nothing to drive in until the Morris came along. We bought it for £115 and sold it back to the same garage McAlister & Brown some years later for the same amount.

Around 1955/56 the Home Guard was resurrected by Winston Churchill who was in office again as Prime Minister. Units comprised cadres and only a limited number, all officers and NCOs were enrolled. Joining was fairly well organised and security clearance had to be accepted beforehand. I was initially taken on as a sergeant after security clearance, a bit of a disappointment since I was a 2nd Lt. in the wartime Home Guard. Subsequently I was commissioned and was soon made Captain and Adjutant of the 1st Hants Regiment, H.G. This was a commission which was acknowledged and the East Yorkshire Regimental Association has always referred to me as Captain ever since. We had headquarters at Beaumont Barracks, Aldershot, an old cavalry barracks. We had a

Above: xx - Viscount G-AHRF, flown for Decca evaluation.

Right: xxi - Decca Suppressed Aerial. Far right: Decca test rig, 1951.

full-time officer – Major Beaston and the C.O. was Lt. Col Sergeant – a JP. Eventually my father joined us, particularly as he realised that one of our main activities was shooting. He won several spoons, not having lost his old touch. We fired on all of the Aldershot Ranges and at Bisley. I won a pool bull there with a .303 having hit a one inch square at 200 yards. We fired Bren machine guns and had Vickers gun instruction. I was able to attend the live fire demonstrations of infantry, artillery and aircraft ground attack by Venoms near Warminster – the School of Infantry. I had an officer's identity card.

We attended a rifle competition against the 4 Battalion (TA) Hampshire Regiment at Winchester. Renée fired .22 – her favourite, and won a teapot first prize.

During the various shooting escapades, I managed to collect several tankards, medals and spoons. Some sixteen rifles with hundreds of rounds of ammunition were on my charge and on occasion I had to hold them all at home prior to a match. Imagine such a thing being possible in the climate of today, less than 50 years later.

Eventually the sad day came when we stood down. My battle dress is still up in the roof as a reminder of the unit and days when one felt one was 'doing one's bit'. The paperwork handing over was much more than setting up the unit.

1956 brought the great change and reward for studying and work in the Department. I was called for interview for Senior Scientific Officer. If successful if would mean the double jump of promotion and transfer to the Scientific Class – only available to graduates. I found it a good interview, the Board chairman being Donald Reid who was a Division Leader at Farnborough. It was surprising to receive an invitation to recap on my career to date when I mentioned the Weegy Board the questioner said "did you design that?" I was staggered to realise that it was known about to a wider number of people than those directly concerned. In 1991 at the RAF Mess, Farnborough cocktail party, a previous Group Captain (COEF) Downey after meeting him for the first time for many years, also mentioned 'the gadget with magnets'.

It was usual to send scientists from the Establishment on a two or three week attachment to one of the armed services. This was to ensure that their research and development programmes would contain an operational reality. My attachments in two cases both required a visit to the Royal Navy, in fact to two aircraft carriers. In 1956 I joined HMS Eagle and we sailed for Gibraltar and it sailed to Suez for the ill-fated campaign there. The people attached were required to participate actively in various tasks on board. As we sailed southward, the ship's company changed their black caps for white-topped headgear. On a Saturday morning I looked over the stern to see hundreds of little black blobs in the sea. They were the unwanted caps thrown overboard.

One of my tasks was to help an aircrew instrument fitter change the airspeed indicator on a Sea Hawk jet fighter. The benefit of my being able to understand difficulties in operation of crew dealing with silly design became clear to me immediately. Extraction of the faulty instrument required access to the rear of the unit. This could be achieved only if one sat on the cockpit floor. To do this meant that the ejector seat had to be removed. To remove the seat needed the movement of the aircraft to the other end of the ship's length of the hangar. Several other aircraft had to be moved so that our Sea Hawk could be positioned under a roof mounted crane. It all took a long time just to get access to four small nuts and screws. We were encouraged to make a report on our return to RAE. Mine was very to the point.

xxii - HMS Eagle, 21 April 1956, in the Bay of Biscay, speed 30 knots. Photographed from Westland S56 Helicopter.

Other items in my subsequent paper highlighted the poor design of the equipment. Some of the mobile units on wheels could not be moved along the flight deck, because the small wheels were too tiny to allow the equipment to cross the arrester cables needed to bring aircraft to a standstill on landing.

In another case I found equipment too big to go down hatches. This meant that units would have to be moved the length of the ship to allow access to the next deck.

The Suez crisis arose while were in the Bay of Biscay. It was decided that two colleagues and myself would have to return to England from Gibraltar. One morning, I was on the flight deck and I heard an announcement on the address system, but I could not identify the message. Soon after I could hear a helicopter but noticed I was alone. A hand grabbed me from behind and I was pulled under cover. I discovered that the message had instructed all personnel to evacuate the flight deck while a photograph was being taken of Ark Royal travelling at full speed. That picture is reproduced here.

While in Gib I learned a lot about the Royal Navy. A Commander was detailed to act as a chaperone. He took us across the border into Spain one night, a very enlightening experience! I was so interested to see the guard changing by a Scottish Regiment at the border, followed by a similar ceremony on the Spanish side.

Another Royal Navy visit was to Hal Far, Malta. It was a tremendous experience. I flew with the Sea Venom two seat fighter in mock air combat. The 'G' forces were about all I could stand. I was dressed in full immersion suit and all of the kit needed for ejector operation, including bone dome etc. The start up and taxi before take off was delayed, and in the hot sun we were sweating profusely before we began the exercise.

I had the opportunity of flying and handling a Whirlwind helicopter from Hal Far to the Gozo end of Malta. An exciting exercise was my transfer to the carrier HMS Centaur. I flew in the rear seat of a Meteor twin jet from Malta to Sardinia. I was then met by a Fairey Gannet turbo prop aircraft out to Centaur at sea, my first carrier landing. By strange coincidence the pilot was an old Farnborough Grammar School boy.

Centaur sailed into Malta. A cocktail party was arranged by several ladies such as UK wives in quarters. The naval hospitality was tremendous. I had a DJ but not a white jacket. I was loaned one straightaway. On being introduced to one of the ladies by an officer she said to me, "not Renée's husband?" Another longshot.

One afternoon the aircrew took me aboard a launch out of Har Far; the jetty at Kalafrana, which had been a flying boat base. We towed a sled and chaps took it in turn to do water skiing. When my turn came, the chaps started shaking the towrope. I fell in the water but rope looped round my ankle pulling me under, still moving fast. Green water filled my lungs and I had to be rescued and revived.

The most alarming exercise on Centaur was when I was positioned with the catapult launching officer. I stood in front of him, between the two catapults at the bow. The jets would increase to take-off power. He would indicate to the pilot to launch and tap me on the shoulder to lean away to let the wing pass over us both. He would then tap the other shoulder when to lean away from No. 2 aircraft. The noise was tremendous. The 'goofing platform' was lined with chaps waiting to see if I would be knocked over into the Mediterranean.

The advent of SSO produced an immediate change in the job, Johnnie Johnson, my division leader and Caradoc's boss, advised me that within 2 weeks I would transfer to the Aerial Group. When I heard about the SSO I was called to see Mc Petrie; Johnnie was there. They seemed surprised that I was surprised that I had been successful.

The transfer, still within 160 Building, was a culture shock. I was second in seniority to Tom Blackband, that much revered PSO. My four years with him involved contact with such brilliant people as Dr. Lloyd Jones, who became a Deputy Director RAE and Dr. Boyd Burgess, later a Deputy Chief Scientific Officer (DCSO) at Malvern.

Tom Blackband was a unique person, extremely well educated and a devout Roman Catholic. In addition to being one of the worlds leading authorities upon aerial, or as is often called antenna design Tom had many other talents. He had a passion for butterflies and would go to

P160 Building. Our Aerial Lab. Donald Hirst on the ladder, my office is top right hand corner. (Crown Copyright MoD)

enormous trouble to extend his collection. More of that later. He was also a very knowledgeable expert on old coins and could identify almost any British type.

Tom had a great sense of humour. He brought a pint tankard into the lab one day and, while we all sat around a large table in the centre of the huge lab in our tea break, said, "Let me show you how to get quarts into a pint pot". He then produced a quantity of quartz crystals and poured them into the tankard. He became a great authority in Advisory Group Aerospace Research and Development (AGARD) and chaired international aerial conferences.

If ever he wished to have one into his office to take issue on a point, he would invariably leave one with the feeling that he really blamed himself rather than the person on the mat. He did not drive a car, mainly due to a problem with one of his hands. He remained a PSO for over 21 years, indeed he had a party to mark the occasion in the RAE Mess. He should have been given a merit Senior Principal Scientific Officer (SPSO) rank time and time again, but somewhere or other someone must have decided to bypass him, it was a great injustice. His son, Michael, was an Air Traffic Officer with the Civil Aviation Authority at Farnborough for some years.

The V bomber force was about to join the RAF squadrons and I was immediately plunged into the problems of aerial design and installation of jamming aerials for them all. The designs had been started by people such as John Asteraki and whose nose must have been put out of joint somewhat by my taking the job over and pinching his small office on the top floor balcony.

Much of the work upon aerial design was conducted at Lasham on a site at the south side of the airfield. Large models of various aircraft type such as the V bombers, Valiant, Vulcan and Victor, were made of wood in the RAE woodwork shops at Farnborough and then covered with a copper skin. The models were some 6 feet in span. Scale model aerials were fitted to the models in the appropriate position for test. Depending upon the scale and the radio frequency of the actual full-scale transmission, an oscillator was contained within the model to radiate or receive on an equivalent scaled up radio frequency ten times the full scale frequency or in other words a wavelength of one tenth of the operational wavelength.

The model was mounted on a turntable, sometimes remotely controlled to put the aerials into any desired altitude. A receiver and recorders were mounted some distance away to allow a radiation pattern of the aerial or polar diagram, as it is sometimes called, to be drawn on the recorder. To achieve the very high frequencies required oscillators such as the Klystron. We operated the models in the K, L and other frequency bands, the most ambitious being O band which didn't work very well.

There were many problems associated with these aerial ranges in those days but they were dealt with excellently by Alec Stembridge and his team, all under the experienced and benevolent eye of Tom Blackband.

On one wet day we were due to demonstrate one of my experiments to a crowd of VIPs who arrived by bus from Farnborough. The bus stopped on the Lasham airfield and Johnnie Johnson led the visitors across the grass towards our range as the rain fell. While they were some yards off, the transmitter in the model blew up, probably due to water seepage. It took quite a bit of ad libbing to talk my way out of the situation.

Some very serious work was conducted at Lasham. During the later 1950s the Russian Sputnik Satellite went into orbit. A satellite monitoring station was set up in the old airfield fire station to record transmissions from the US Transit navigation system. This grew until most work now appears to be conducted at nearby Oakhanger. There were many amusing incidents at Lasham, especially those involving Joe Edwards our, mechanic and jack-of-all-trades who had been the Department for years, in fact the same chap who had worked with us at the old wartime GCI station on Farnborough airfield years before. There was also a chap who acted as a watchman at Lasham. He was referred to as the Drain Man. The lads such as Cooper and Mountain would climb out onto the roof of the old control tower and stuffs rags down the chimney of his stove to smoke the Drain Man out. He would get very irate at this naughty prank.

A film was made of the Lasham scene, it even included a visit at lunchtime by the section to the Golden Pot pub. Perhaps Alec Stembridge knows what happed to the film. I only saw it shown once. I believe that RAE Printing Department made it.

One interesting example of Civil Service bureaucracy occurred just before I left Farnborough for my Washington posting. Pete Mountain who was working on the Lasham airfield on one of the test ranges pointed out that it took several minutes to walk back to the main building for tools such as a spanner which might be needed. He requested a bicycle and I agreed to get one from Transport Department. I was duly offered a 'yellow peril' RAF type yellow bike but told that it was to be recorded on my flying clothing card as a personal issue. The bike arrived at Lasham but within days the loose stone track had caused a puncture. I was asked for a puncture outfit but was told by Transport Department that it was a fitter's job to mend the puncture; my staff were not permitted to do the job. A truck with fitter was sent the 16 miles to Lasham to collect the bike which was returned to Farnborough. We heard no more, neither did we have our bike.

When I was due to go to the States I was required to hand in all my flying kit which included the bike. I was instructed to produce the bike. I sent one of my chaps to the back of the old 4 Squadron black sheds near Cody's Tree where there were lots of yellow perils. He brought one back and the stores people were satisfied. He then returned the bike to where he had found it. The letter of the law had been satisfied.

Within a couple of weeks or so of joining Tom Blackband's team he said, "before you came we had no aircraft involved in the programme. Already you have programmes with almost all of the Radio Department aircraft!"

I managed to have full-scale aerials fitted to Hastings WD480 and we began flight tests to obtain radiation patterns. These were flown over the Imber Range on Salisbury Plain. We then made installations on the actual V bombers and I managed 30 hours on each type. We did a low run in the Victor at the Imber and an operator photographed us as we passed – as illustrated.

Work began on the Valiant. We had to go to Wisley airfield and use one of the early versions of the aircraft. An instructional course on the baling out procedure was required since only the two pilots had ejection seats. A disastrous accident to a prototype had resulted in fatalities. One had to evacuate the aircraft through a side door in sequence of crew members. The door had a protective screen like a sugar scoop to take the first blast of the slipstream. My position indicated that I would have to go out first, but Jim Arthy, my right hand man, said "Freddy, if I even have to tread on your face, I'm going out first!" So much for authority.

We had two exciting sorties in the Valiant. The first was when the Maxarette brakes caught fire on landing. We had fire engines trailing after us as smoke trailed down the runway. On another occasion, the undercarriage failed to come down. Every option was tried but to no avail. A radio call requested someone to ask the drawing office designers at Vickers for ideas. Meanwhile as we orbited around Witley, the Vickers staff began to gather outside the hangar to watch the fun. While this was going on, the navigator put all his charts etc in his navigator bag and calmly proceeded to lay out a pack of cards on his desk and began to play patience. When I queried him he said "I got you all home now the rest of the job is for the pilot". The wheels did come down eventually and all was well.

Flight in the Vulcan went smoothly although I wondered if the RAF and Avros would accept the enormous modification I proposed to house the jamming aerials.

I had ordered some Frog plastic 1/92nd models of the three V bombers and with a theodolite determined the best installation positions. I was amused when a stores officer questioned the legitimacy of the requisition for the models. He must have known about my hobby and large model collection. The Vulcan installation was tried on a large model and comprised a large ground plane covering the gap between two of the engines. I was to see an operational aircraft at Goose Bay, Newfoundland some years later containing my complete modification. It was the first indication that I had that the design had been accepted.

During the first years of the 21st Century, a group lead by a great entrepreneur, David Walton, set about rebuilding a Vulcan to flying standard. I have seen this aircraft many times at Dave's airfield and museum at Bruntingthorpe near the village of Walton where our daughter Carol lives. I was so pleased to find that my aerial installation was still there in between the starboard engines.

An Avro test pilot called Blackman flew us on several occasions in the Vulcan. Normally we embarked at the ARL site at RAE. I was asking him to bank at various angles one day and suddenly everything on my bench took off. I asked what he was doing and he said that it seemed easier to complete the roll in order to level up again.

The test pilot in the Victor was Heseltine – a very experienced and well-known person. One great advantage from our point of view was that the chaps in the rear could see out over the shoulders of the pilots. The other two types, Valiant and Vulcan merely had a couple of small portholes, one on either side.

One day in 1958 Johnnie Johnson asked me if I would like to learn to fly. Although I was right at the top of the age limit for the Civil Service six week course, he managed to get me accepted. I went to Thruxton; more about that later.

xxiv - Low fly past in the Victor Imber range, then home to Radlett.

In September 1959 Tom Blackband suggested that I should visit the USA to liaise with their industry on several technical aspects of our aerial design work and to attend a conference on aerials in Ohio. This was to be my first trip to the USA. I first visited some places in Canada before arriving in Washington DC where I called at the K Street home of the Defence Research Staff. The present British Embassy Building on Massachusetts Avenue was still under construction. I met Donald Reid, the Assistant Director, who had chaired my SSO Board. He seemed very keen to get me to do a tour in the US and hinted that he was altering the job specification since he had no offers from PSOs to fill a post. He intended adjusting the vacancy to PSO or SSO.

Incidentally I flew out to New York from the UK in a BOAC DC7 aircraft before going up to Canada. At Heathrow the terminal buildings were of the portacabin type with brown lino on the floor. The flight took 12 hours and the smell of bacon and eggs cooking at breakfast time lingers on.

The trip included a review of work in California and Chicago. I was to experience my first flights in the Boeing 707 and found that take off run so long that I wondered if we were going by road.

In 1960 Renée very sadly had a stillborn baby. It was a tragedy which was hard to take but especially to Renée. I had been asked twice if I would take the Washington post but had postponed a decision. By the autumn I was asked again and Renée and I were invited to tea by the

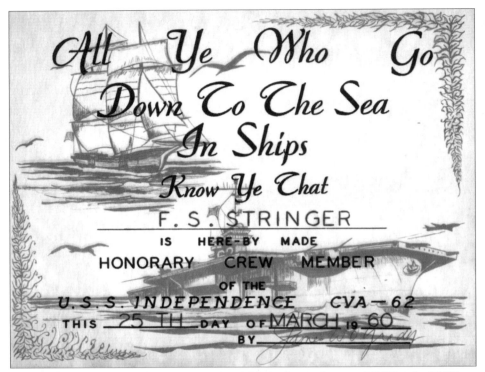

xxv - Honorary Crew Member of the USS Independence, 25 March 1960.

Deputy Director of RAE, Sam Follett. We both felt that it was a sort of once over for each of us and it seemed to seal the decision which we finally endorsed one evening while sitting on the step outside our lounge French window. Thus ended my first 19 years with the RAE and Radio Department.

After 3½ years in the Aerial Group, in March 1960 I was asked to refer back to my navigation work. An international committee had met in Paris at the Palais de Chalieux. The purpose of the meeting was to decide upon the international selection of the British Decca System of Navigation or the VOR/DME (Visual Omni Range/Distance Measuring Equipment) based upon Tacan techniques. Apparently the UK delegates had indicated that the VOR/DME System had problems. The US wanted VOR/DME. Because I had been involved with both research programmes, I was sent for by the UK team. When I arrived the US delegates asked for a delay while they sent for a CAA man. We both knew each other, in fact Al and I were good friends. When he arrived he said he had been roused from his bed in the States and told to fly to Paris.

The technical argument I raised concerned the possible interference by DME with the IFF transponders. Al and I argued, apparently above the heads of the delegates. We were told to go into the corridor and decide what should be done as proof of interference one way or the other.

After agreement between us, I reported that we needed a comprehensive test. When asked what do you need? I replied that I wanted to use a full aircraft carrier complement and exercises done at sea. I was surprised to receive agreement. Consequently I was allowed to use the huge USS Independence for the trial with the FAA team in attendance as well as myself. I flew to the USA and on to the Naval Station at Norfolk, Virginia. I was flown with the FAA chaps out to sea in a twin propeller driven Tracker aircraft. We landed on the carrier. It really was huge. There were escalators between decks.

I received a great welcome aboard. The first job was to be interviewed on the ship's TV and Radio. It was like a small town. Food was wonderful but like all USN ships it was dry. A milestone in the number of aircraft landings was achieved and celebrated while I was on board – with a birthday cake. Officers spoke to me wistfully about times they had been attached to the Royal Navy where alcohol is not a crime.

The exercises went well and I watched them on radar. I was shadowed all the time by a minder. I was satisfied and although I would have liked a British system such as the very accurate Decca, the VOR/DME was eventually adopted. I use it everyday many years later and I am so grateful for it.

I enjoyed watching night flying while positioned on the 'goofing platform'. After the exercises I was made an honorary member of the crew. My certificate is 'illustrated'.

Chapter 6

FLYING TRAINING

In 1948 I had joined the Community Flying Club. They had a Piper Cub at Woodley. I did about 5 hours dual there but did not go solo. It took too long to get there since I travelled from Farnborough by bike, train, bus and on foot each time. All afternoon for about 30 minutes airborne. A Polish man and a lady instructed me, but I did not more until 1958 in September when I started a proper course at Thruxton under the Ministry scheme. I had to start again from scratch.

As mentioned earlier Johnnie Johnson arranged for me to go to Thruxton to take a six week flying course. Having been rejected years before for a course by the then Head of Department, S.B. Gates, I was extremely pleased. I had a medical examination at RAE then in September 1958 set off in our Hillman car to the airfield on the Hampshire, Wiltshire border. Before going that morning I had an altercation with a belligerent old fellow on a bicycle near the Grammar School who claimed I had cut in front of him. Actually I was nowhere near him so I suggested he speak to the police. I went home and called the police first. They seemed to have met him before.

On arrival at Thruxton I went in to the Control Tower and asked for the boss, Squadron Leader Dorian Webb. He wasn't there but a Squadron Leader John Heaton was, and he welcomed me and became my instructor. He was the Chief Flying Instructor (CFI). I met the other chaps on the course as they arrived and noted that some were from headquarters and others from other establishments. There were 6 or 7 of us. Additionally there were several West Indians mostly training under their own finances. Among the instructors were Wing Commander Ramsey Smith, and Peter Gush – both farmers – Peter had a pig farm, Captain Smith known as 'Sprocket' – ex army and later Fred Mercer. I flew with them all but John was my main instructor. Ramsey sent me on my first solo and Fred did my Private Pilot's Licence (PPL) General Flying Test. At my 80th birthday party, Ron Elder, Head of Flight Crew Licensing Civil Aviation Authority (CAA) kindly presented me with a copy of Fred Mercer's report on that test. He also gave me a copy of my Assistant Flying Instructor original test. It seems that the CAA keep every record.

I had the opportunity to get my hands on to the controls of odd RAE aircraft unofficially over the years. They included Anson, Oxford, Wellington, Magister, Piper Cub and Aircoupe. They were all very unofficial and for fleeting moments only. The Cub time was a little longer but nothing much.

I therefore welcomed a sortie or two with Mike Cross and another pilot in a Chipmunk just before setting off to learn to fly. The aircraft equipping the Wiltshire School of Flying at Thruxton were Tiger Moths and mostly

Jackaroos. The latter was a converted Tiger Moth with enclosed cockpit and four seats. The undercarriage track and fuselage were a little wider than the Tiger. The first pilot sat in front for solo and dual unlike the Tiger where student and first pilot for solo sat in the rear cockpit.

There was no radio and intercom used Gosport tubes. Starting was always with hand swinging of the propeller. We fed in a dining room, still used but modified today, in the old wartime control tower. Sleeping accommodation was in a Nissen hut and boy was it cold! Ground instruction was also in a Nissen hut.

My first flying lesson took place with John Heaton one lovely evening in a Jackaroo. We rushed through some of the exercises and he suggested that he would cut corners based on my performance during the course. I suppose we did cut corners because I went solo in 3 hours 35 minutes. John tried to demonstrate recovery from a bounce on landing but I did not like to introduce the bounce, so John bounced for me and then said "recover".

My first solo one morning came unexpectedly when Ramsey Smith got into the aircraft. After a few circuits he got out of the aircraft G-ANFY (for Freddy) and said off you go. We were in the middle of the grass area. He noted another aircraft landing and in an effort to attract my attention, banged the lead of his Gosport tube on the top of the fuselage near the tail. The bang made me jump not knowing what was the cause of the bang

I sang all round the circuit on that first solo, coming in to land past the control tower and Ramsey said it was a nice wheel landing. I thought I had made it a three point, he said, "don't come over the top of the windsock, you might have hit it"! He told me about a chap who once at some airfield or other did just that and spiralled down it to the ground.

The rest of the course was sheer enjoyment. Another instructor joined John Heaton and Ramsey Smith to continue the course. This was Peter Gush the pig farmer, like Ramsey. The local industry seemed to depend to a large extent on pig farming. Peter was a chap who would put up with no nonsense although he was pretty kind to me. I remember crosswind landings in the Jackaroo; we landed out of wind and he taught me the 'yaw as you flair' technique. After a couple of goes he said "Right, now do some on your own". I have put my progress sheet in one of the family historical volumes.

My first cross-country flight was with Peter. It was a short triangular course map reading exercise. He would say, "what is the village down there?" I must have replied correctly because that was the only dual cross-country instruction I received. I was then sent off on my own.

Some of the training was in a Tiger Moth or two. One of them which I later flew on my own was G-ACEZ, coloured silver wings and green fuselage. It had been the very same aircraft in which Geoffrey Tyson had done his extraordinary feat at the Alan Cobham Air Displays – his

National Air Days – by picking up a handkerchief, sitting on a small frame, with his wingtip as he flew past when I had seen him do this at Richmond in Yorkshire in around 1933/34. It was written off in a prang in the late 1960s.

Ramsey Smith did stalls with me in the Tiger Moth and he included the alarming exercise of stopping the propeller in flight then making me dive steeply, switch on the magnetos, throttle set and the engine would start. After we landed Ramsey said "you did the right thing by jerking the control column backward slightly to assist the airflow to start the engine". Actually, and I did not confess it, it was nervous twitch which caused my involuntary hand movements.

Ground study was in one of the huts and included talks by Fred Mercer, a young chap who appeared to be the only instructor who had not been in the Forces. Usually this occurred in poor weather, though there was not much of it that September. I recall a day with blue skies but a very strong wind. John Heaton said to a lot of us, "despite your enthusiasm to get into the air, you are not going to do it today; it's too windy, so off you all go and walk round the perimeter track!" So off we went.

I had gone solo before the rest of the chaps and John thought that I would get my PPL first. I did, but before that there was still a lot to do. Fortunately Ground Examinations were not a requirement, but the qualifying cross-country flight certainly was required. John Heaton agreed that I should do this on a Saturday. It took most of the day! My route was Thruxton to Weston Super Mare. Then to Kidlington, Oxford and back to Thruxton. No radio, no navigation aids and only a magnetic compass. Incidentally no intercom didn't matter since I was on my own and Gosport tubes served no purpose. I had guessed the wind and did some preliminary dead reckoning calculations and I then set off on a fairly nice day. I found Weston Super Mare all right, but wondered why I passed an Avro Anson in the circuit going the other way. After landing I found that the signal square indicated that the circuits were right-handed, not left-handed! In my anxiety to land carefully and safely at this airfield I saw for the first time, I had not noticed the signal square black and yellow arrow. I had been more concerned to note the wind direction indicated by the landing 'T'. Nobody complained, so I booked in and out. I recall that landing fees were not required. I had never landed at another airfield on the Thruxton course, even dual.

The trip to Kidlington took a long time with an indicated airspeed of 65-70 knots. 'Smokey Joe', the chimney near the airfield eventually heaved into sight – I had been given that piece of vital information by Sprocket. The grass landing surface presented no problems but I found taxiing on the tarmac without brakes and only a tailskid was tricky. I sensibly refuelled but cannot recall whether I paid or if it was invoiced. Probably the latter. Another long haul to Thruxton into the sun took most of the afternoon – I had not eaten. There was a lot of activity at the

xxvi - The Jackaroo.

airfield and everyone was engrossed in Saturday afternoon programmes. I found John Heaton and proudly told him that I had completed the qualifying cross country and he just said "Good" and left it at that. He left me with the impression that he had really forgotten about me and the qualifying flight.

I was next faced with my final flight test but had not got sufficient dual hours. So John would get into the back of a Jackaroo after breakfast with his newspaper while I flew him around to get the necessary hours. For my flight test I was assigned to Fred Mercer. I had never flown with him before. The weather was not too good as we took off. He asked me to do a number of exercises, one of which was a stall off a climbing turn, which no on had ever showed me – before. The weather gradually clamped as we were in the Romsey area, when Fred with a touch of alarm in his voice said he was lost – or words to that effect. After several minutes flying approximately northwards, I saw the army camp near the Andover – Basingstoke road junction with the main road to Newbury from Southampton.

I suggested to Fred that I could navigate him back to Thruxton, which I did. On reaching the circuit a relieved instructor/examiner said that he would land the aircraft. I was then congratulated on return to the club buildings and advised that I had got my PPL. I then surprised him by saying that one thing had been missed; he had not asked me to land the aircraft! This came as a bit of a shock but it apparently did not alter his decision and he still said that I had passed.

I still had about nearly three weeks of my course to go so I enjoyed myself flying at Government expense. Renée and Carol came down to

Ramsey Smith's farm for a while and we spent about a week there. He lived about 1½ miles away.

During that time Sheila Scott came to the airfield and started a course of flying instruction. John Heaton was her instructor and this glamorous lady became quite a personality. She eventually got her licence and bought a Jackeroo, G-A PAM – blue and silver. The story of Sheila's exploits before and after this period have been related in books and on television, more later in this narrative, right up to the sad time when I scattered her ashes from the air over Thruxton.

We had some memorable celebrations in the bar after flying. On one occasion after it was getting dark, most of the West Indian contingent had gone to the cinema in Andover. Fred Mercer complained that one of the chaps had not booked in after landing before going out and the aircraft had been put away in the hangar. The telephone rang and a policeman asked for the CFI. He reported a Jackaroo upside down in a field north of Thruxton just next to another airfield. In fact the pilot was not hurt but had overflown Thruxton having missed it and did not recognise the ground to the north. As it was getting dark he made a precautionary landing; much to Fred Mercer's surprise, we were one aircraft short at the hangar and no one had noticed.

The opportunity arose one Sunday morning for me to accompany Peter Gush in a Proctor aircraft on an army cooperation exercise. I accepted the invitation, mainly to get another type in my logbook. After flying around for some time, partly over cloud, Peter then said, "where are we!" I said "I don't know". He then got very angry and told me that I was supposed to be navigating. I said that it was the first that I had heard of it. We did not speak to each other for quite a while but got back safely.

John Heaton gently punched me in the chest one evening and said "that's where you like flying". From such a CFI those words were very important to me.

I joined the Wiltshire Flying Club and when the course finished I was able to fly both Jackaroos and Tiger Moths for many months. I took Renée and Carol and my father. Dad had never flown before but was very, very enthusiastic. He struggled into a Sidcot flying suit and came with me in one of the Tiger Moths. Incidentally during my course, on a still evening, we would practice short field landings approaching from the west at a very slow speed, then get almost below the level of the airfield in the low valley and just drop onto the grass near the parked aircraft stopping, without brakes of course, in just a few yards. Instructors such as Ramsey would find themselves with a pupil at the Eastern end of the airfield and actually fly back to the control tower, rather than taxi.

I saw John Heaton check out a Tiger Moth and complete the air test with a spin. He then landed directly upon recovery and stopped the aircraft in line with the others; and all of this without brakes.

John was very dedicated and kept flying when he had flu. I believe he contracted pneumonia and sadly died. That was some time during the 1960s I believe. He liked his drink and enjoyed relating escapades during the War when I believe that he was in Africa.

I flew Alice, and two of her children, Hilary and Yvonne in the Jackaroo. Alice was Renée's sister-in-law. Tom Blackband my boss also flew with me but complained of the 'g' when I did some turns. I think, or rather hope, he enjoyed it on the whole.

Dad & I would drive down to Thruxton (no motorways then) in our Hillman Minx (Jumbo). We once ran out of petrol and had to walk to a nearby garage to get some. A great adventure was a Jackaroo trip to Lympne from Thruxton one Saturday with Dad and Brian Cookesley from our group at RAE. A flask of coffee and maps etc did not leave much room in the small cabin. On changing a fold in the map, I knocked the coffee over – causing chaos in such a small space. On return I had a duff magneto. I telephoned the airfield but was told, come back on one! Inexperience and enthusiasm won the day and I returned. On another occasion I had an exhaust gasket blow. What a noise. On one of these trips, maybe it was the Lympne one, I decided to get the aircraft back onto the ground quickly. Sprocket came to me afterwards to complain that I had cut in on him. I explained that I had an emergency and he left it at that. Without radio things could be difficult, and still can be.

I continued to fly at Thruxton during the time when I was stationed in Washington when I was back in England or on duty. I have some lovely slides of photographs I took while flying the Jackaroos, over the Wiltshire countryside. In those days you could fly at 2000 ft straight along Southampton Water with no calling for radar cover. There was usually no other traffic in sight.

The Washington posting gave me the opportunity to fly in America, particularly during the last year there, but I shall recount that in a later chapter. However, my flying continued upon return to England in August 1963 and goes into another chapter.

I joined the club at Fairoaks and flew the Piper Colt and qualified on the Auster. Dad asked the instructor if he could sit in the back while I did the conversion to type. That was agreed but when I was told to go off on my own Dad surprised us by asking if he could come too. He did, and showed no apprehension at all.

The people at Fairoaks were very nice indeed. Wing Commander Cyril Arthur was the CFI. He had learned to fly on Maurice Farman Shorthorns during World War I. He had to make a forced landing on his first solo because a cylinder fell out of the engine.

Fairoaks was all grass at the time with a high part in the middle – which surprisingly was conducive to mud and water in wet weather. The Tiger Club had one or two aircraft at Fairoaks including a Tiger Moth. One of the instructors was a Tiger Club check pilot and he gave me the necessary air test in a Tiger to be eligible for membership. It was completed satisfactorily although he said that I had overdone the recovery from a spin having pushed the stick too far forward resulting in a vertical dive before recovery.

A navigator friend of mine flew several times in Tiger Moths at Fairoaks with me, also Dick Bullock from the USA during a very wet September with floods in Chobham on the way by road. I was able to fly a Turbulent quite a lot and did many flights in various aircraft with Dad who had made a terrific recovery from a stroke he had while we were in the USA. He used a stick for walking but dumped it before struggling onto the aircraft. His flight in a Condor required two ground crew to lift him out.

If the weather was bad, Dad would get very excited if we flew and no one else did. He flew some 200 times with me and only flew with Ivor or myself. On one occasion he was very chuffed to be with me in a Colt and Ivor in loose formation in another one. He had got ready to fly that last day before New Year's Eve, a Saturday in 1968. The manageress said to him in the lounge of the Wycombe Hotel in Alexandra Road, Farnborough, where he was living at the time, "it's not a very nice day Major Stringer!" Dad said "Never mind, we are going flying later on!" He picked up the Daily Telegraph to read as he sat there and he died.

When I collected his very sparse belongings, I found a notebook in which he had been making notes on flying lessons. He would enjoy controlling the aircraft from time to time. Once in a Colt, as we touched down my seat shot backwards. I said, "I can't see". He said, "it's alright, I can!" On another trip the rather shock absorbers on the Colt and the grass surface at Fairoaks were collectively giving us the familiar shaking as we did a touch and go. Dad's spectacle case in his hip pocket made him flinch. I shouted "Alright?" He said "alright", getting the wrong message and promptly took over and took off!

The benefit of doing checks was demonstrated several times. I was doing a pre-flight check on a Turbulent, a very small single seat aircraft; all seemed satisfactory until I went round the rear of the aircraft when I found that the fin and rudder had been smashed. The probable cause was a confrontation with a Beech King Air, not by direct contact but as a result of a powerful slipstream as the larger aircraft taxied past. A proper ground check of an aircraft before flight is always taught but obvious damage can be overlooked quite easily.

A notable incident at Fairoaks was when a very good ground engineer, a very helpful and friendly chap, I forget his name, was running up a Colt on the tarmac. A very strong gust of wind picked up the aircraft which then turned over and fell onto the ground upside down. The engineer managed to switch the engine off before he hit the deck. The propeller stopped horizontally and damage was minimised. Quick reaction and thinking by him.

xxvii - 'Turbulent Type' Fairoaks, 30 June 1966.

The Club Secretary at Fairoaks was a nice chap called 'Dutch' Holland. Bill Laslett was an instructor; he had been in my form at the Aldershot County High School in 1934-36. We often talked of those days. He told me once he had a student freeze on the controls during a spin. He saw the ground coming up fast and had to put both feet on the rudder to counter the student's foot pressing on the wrong side. They recovered from the spin, but Bill was pretty shaken. I would fly the Tiger Club aircraft over to Redhill sometimes when the Club was holding a display. The return trip could present a problem due to weather.

On one very memorable occasion, I was advised that the people at Fairoaks wanted the Turbulent G-ARJZ back there from Redhill before dark. I called the office on the telephone to get an actual weather report and was told it was OK. I took off and all was well until I crossed the Hogs Back when the weather clamped and it started to rain. I looked round but a return to Redhill seemed out of the question as clouds and poor visibility with low stratus enveloped the whole area. I descended to stay in sight of the surface. My goggles began to fill with water and, worse still, the engine seemed to be experiencing carburettor icing. As I applied carb heat the power dropped sufficiently to cause me to descend further. I couldn't see very far so I turned towards Farnborough where I knew that I could effect a safe landing. However I suddenly caught sight of Ash Church and knew I could follow the railway towards Brookwood and Woking. I was getting lower and came to the Tunnel Hill railway tunnel. I climbed and searched for the other end. I found it then crept along the line but was worried about my height when I could see the railway signal lights. I passed Brookwood Station but on approaching Woking, decided that I must return to Brookwood which I did. On arrival at the station I turned right at the crossroads then followed the road to Chobham to ensure that I would not stray into the Heathrow Air Traffic Zone. I went past Chobham, found Fairoaks, throttled back and flaired to land. I found the airfield closed due to weather. I kicked the tyres and reported in. So much for an actual weather report.

I could not understand why other members did not find a notice on the clubhouse amusing. It said children under two not admitted. I considered that children under two couldn't read. While at Fairoaks I decided that I would very much like to become an Assistant Flying Instructor. I joined forces with Peter Coyle, an Air Training Corps Officer. Our instructor was Sid Parker. He had been an instructor during the war and was very good indeed. He did not suffer fools gladly and really put us through it. For instance, he made me fly the Tiger Moth, in which we did the course, under the hood during a circuit. Just basic instruments. I was only allowed to raise the hood when on short finals. I remember we took off due north, the airfield was all grass in those days and I found the whole circuit somewhat alarming. I think Sid must have grinned to himself all the way round because he could see.

Sid could get quite exasperated with us on occasion. I pulled his leg one day during forced landing without power. He pointed out a field as a demonstration forced landing area. I said I couldn't identify the one he meant. He kept on pointing to it rolling the aircraft to assist identification with his voice getting more and more rattled until I gave in and said I could see it. By that time the Tiger Moth was nearly upside down, Sid said that he never swore at students, but I proved him wrong that day.

The patter caused me concern. I would drive to the airfield saying exercises over to myself. At stopping places drivers alongside would look at me thinking I must have gone barmy.

The day came for Peter and me to fly to Biggin Hill in the Tiger Moth to be examined by Alan (Bunny) Branson. I could not really identify the grass landing strip running due South. I chose what I thought was the right strip, but on reporting to Air Traffic, they asked me why we had landed in the rough! The test went well for both of us with a trip to Redhill and back built in. On the way Bunny said he had control then proceeded to perform aerobatics. Having got it out of his system, he said, "you have control, take me to Redhill". I think he was really testing me for orientation awareness. Pete got his oral exam completed at Biggin Hill but time did not allow for me to do mine so I was invited by Bunny to go to his place of work at a furniture shop, a chain store in Bromley, for the test and tea. It went well with Bunny drawing some very useful diagrams including the aerodynamic aspects of the spin. I have those diagrams to this day.

xviii - Tiger Moth G-ACDC at Redhill.

As my Tiger Club membership allowed me to fly the small contingent of their aircraft at Fairoaks, I took a Tiger Moth G-ARAZ (coloured silver with black registration letters) to a meeting at Old Warden. The weather was very cold and snow showers appeared. I flew from Fairoaks to Kidlington (Oxford) to pick up my brother Ivor. On the way my meagre flight plan flew out of the cockpit. Still, I got to Kidlington and we pressed on to Old Warden. The show was interesting but I was anxious to return early to Fairoaks because of the weather and the daylight problem. I asked to leave before the show finished. It was agreed but I was asked if I would do a display first. I was non-committal about meeting the request. On take off we hit a bump on the grass airfield which chucked the aircraft into the sky. We thought the take-off was enough to interest the crowd and I set course for Kidlington. After leaving Ivor at Kidlington, I recall how cold it was with snowflakes drifting by on my return to Fairoaks. Flying at Redhill gave me the opportunity of flying many types of light aircraft. I was converted onto the Jodel DR1050, a lovely white aircraft with green letters, by Golding-Barrett (G.B.) He wore plus fours and was a very well known character. He chastised me for flying at a different height to his initial instruction but advised me that with the airbrake down the stall was a bit vicious. He climbed out of the aircraft after landing, then said, "now you can stall it, off you go!" So I did – and it was vicious.

I flew three types of Jodel but my favourite was the Puss Moth, green and silver. If only I could have bought it from the Club. It was sold to someone in Canada, I believe. I also flew the Fox Moth; the famous G-ACEJ which was written off at Old Warden some years later after a bad collision with a Cherokee. I flew CEJ at Redhill and at Rochester. The cabin had a fox's head on the bulkhead. The pilot could look through a little window at his two passengers. I took a police friend and his wife in it. The rim of the cockpit was narrow, so one had to squeeze in, but once installed it was quite roomy. An amusing characteristic was that the long distance from the dashboard to the engine meant that the Bowden cable from the engine to the tachometer had enormous slack in it, so that the pointer on the instrument would oscillate considerably when the engine was operating. The Tiger Moth was bread and butter and G-ACDC was flown a lot. It was, and at the time of writing, is the oldest Tiger in existence. The Stampe was a joy to fly, 5 straps to do up and stirrups on the rudder pedals. It was like riding a horse.

I painted a picture of the Stampe and it was accepted as a Tiger Club Christmas Card by Michael Jones, son of the famous Norman Jones founder of the Club. The summer was 1975, very dry and hot, before the famous drought summer of 1976. Nigel and Carol, our daughter, became engaged that summer. I flew Nigel in the Stampe to the spot where I depicted in the painting, then put the aircraft into the same steep climbing turn and said to Nigel, "look you are in the Christmas card!" I flew Carol some time before in a Tiger, the intercom didn't work but by hand signals, she wanted to get back into the air after landing, so we did.

I flew many types of aircraft belonging to the Tiger Club and eventually Michael Jones asked me if I would become a Check Pilot. I was pleased to join this prestigious team of pilots. I checked many pilots over the years. Duty was about every 6 weeks or more, for me on Saturdays. Renée was never too pleased at my departure for a whole day.

The talent of established Tiger Club members was very varied. One German had flown Messerschmitts and Focke-Wulfes in the Luftwaffe, (I painted a picture of Tiger Moth CDC for him as a gift to a girlfriend), he was killed in an air accident in the USA subsequently, I was told. The money from the painting I gave to the East Yorkshire Regimental Association to enable members on hard times to attend the annual reunion dinner. Some of the pilots have become well known. Charles Shea-Simmonds was checked out on a Tiger Moth by me; he has since become a leader of the Royal Aero Club and a display Tiger Moth pilot. One chap claimed 800 hours or more experience. On take-off in the Tiger he swung hard right, I countered this with a lot of left foot pressure on the rudder bar. On landing I asked him why he did not keep straight. He said, "I tried to but the rudder was very stiff," I replied that it was stiff because I was pushing the other way. He was applying the wrong correction and I wondered if he had flown the 800 hours claimed.

Life at Redhill was very pleasant for all members during the 1970s but later on there were many restrictions which grew ever more irksome

xxix - Stampe SV4 G-AWEF over Redhill. F.S.S. painting for a Tiger Club Christmas card.

until the Club left and went to Headcorn. Although I remained a member and check pilot after the move, I had more than enough time to spend with the RAE Aero Club as CFI and DCFI, so I did not fly with them at Headcorn., One of the most exciting aircraft I flew at Redhill was the Rollason Beta prototype racing aircraft. It crashed in a head on collision with a Tiger Moth at a display somewhere subsequently. Many aircraft such as the Condor, Super Cub and others were flown for myself for fun and for checking purposes.

One Saturday I was Duty Pilot. To my horror I saw a Cassut Racer taxi to the western threshold of the E.W. Runway. The wind was from the west so aircraft were landing at the Eastern touchdown. A Tiger Moth was on short finals, neither had radio but miraculously did not collide. I asked the pilot why he went the wrong way. He said because we took off that way yesterday!

Prior to my involvement with Fairoaks and the Tiger Club our stay in the United States from November 1960 to August 1963 (reported in a later chapter) involved quite a lot of flying. On several occasions I returned to the UK on duty and twice on leave when Mum was very ill and after she died. I flew at Thruxton in Jackaroos on these occasions, sometimes

xxx - Tiger Club G-ACDC lands at Redhill, by F.S.S.

with Dad. I used my Kodak Retinette camera I had purchased in the States and took those nostalgic slides from the air. Back in the USA I had to wait for about two years before I could fly there. I took my US Air Law examination at the Federal Aviation Agency offices and fortunately achieved 100% in the multi-choice papers. From then on I could fly there wherever I wanted to go.

Since writing much of this chapter, time spent with the RAE, now the Farnborough Flying Aero Club has increased until now. As DCFI and then CFI, I am teaching PPL students, and Instrument Meteorological Conditions (IMC) also Night Ratings. Additionally I have done checking and conversion. The checks cover a wide variety of pilots, from very inexperienced to RAF and Navy fighter pilots getting their Civil Licences or type ratings. I have done many ground examinations and stamping the Certificates of Experience for them as CAA Authorised Examiner.

Fortunately Mike Bagshaw was the CFI when I was DCFI at Farnborough, with his wealth of experience, Test Pilot, Doctor, G.P. Doctor Test Pilot, Author, Examiner, Chief Medic Aircrew British Airways, ex Squadron Leader, Violinist to say the least, he is a brilliant and a close friend. My first examiner Bunny Branson preceded the late Ron Campbell MBE another close friend, and more recently Rod Jarvis: all very famous aviators and examiners. I have learned so much from them.

I took up instructing again after a check out with Ron at Cranfield, together with Squadron Leader Fred Hambly. We did it in the PA28-140

Cherokee G-A-JG, an aircraft rebuilt by the Bedford apprentices.

My subsequent experiences since becoming a flying instructor and later on examiner, have been many and varied. I have put some of these into the later chapter since they can be associated with many aspects of activities from 1982 onwards, when, after my first RAE retirement, I spent a much greater proportion of my time flying light aircraft.

Chapter 7

WASHINGTON D.C.

The move to Washington was very dramatic. I arranged to let our house to the RAF during my posting, Squadron Leader Alan Pemberton and his wife took on the hiring. He started a 3 year tour at the RAE as a pilot just as we were about to go abroad. We packed a fair amount of stuff but left most of it in the tender care of an agent, then moved out with Carol into the Tumble Down Dick hotel for a few days. We were due to embark on the Queen Mary from Southampton. It was November and the Atlantic could be rough. I sold our almost new Austin A30 to Ivor.

Just before we were due to leave I learned from Dr. Peter Jarmin, our family doctor, that my Mum had terminal cancer. It was decided that I should stay behind for a few days and fly out to the States. Renée and Carol were to sail as planned. I went down by train to Southampton and saw them aboard. First Class cabin and second class dining room. They had a very unhappy crossing. They sailed without me, and the weather was very rough with stormy seas. Arrival at the other end was unhappy too. They travelled by train to Washington from New York and into a flat reserved by the Embassy for staff awaiting more permanent accommodation.

I flew out from Heathrow to New York and then on to Washington. We were not happy in the flat and put all our energy into finding a house. Fortunately we found an ideal one in Bethesda in Ipswich Road. The owner was a charming old gentleman who asked for a very reasonable rent. The house itself was extremely well stocked with furniture and all the gadgets we needed including a dishwasher, which to us in 1960, was a novel attraction, although we didn't use it much.

The new British Embassy building in Massachusetts Avenue in the autumn of 1960 involved a move of the old British Joint Services Mission in 1800 K Street. The unit I joined was the Defence Research Staff and I was the first incumbent of my office on the 5th Floor. My Assistant Director was Ted Forster. Originally when I met Donald Reid on my visit to the USA in 1959 I had been told about the post I occupied but it was advertised at that time to require a Principal Scientific Officer (PSO). I was only an SSO (Senior Scientific Officer). The vacancy notice was changed, presumably at Donald's suggestion as mentioned earlier. He was the chairman of my SSO Board. Two of his staff joined Ted Forster and moved from K Street to the new building; they were Alan Young, A Scotsman, and Charles Philips. I replaced a chap, well known in the Instrument Landing Research field. Adrian Beresford who had moved to the Federal Aviation Agency (FAA) in Washington.

My job comprised liaison between the UK and US on a wide range of avionic research and development. I seemed to gather most things other than radar and communication systems. Alan Young was airborne radar systems and Charles was a communications man from SRDE Christchurch. Alan was an RSRE man (then RRE) from Malvern. Later on Ralph Eades took Charles' place and Fred Holmes followed Alan. Alan left under somewhat unusual circumstances. He joined the John Hopkins University and left the UK Scientific Civil Service and I believe he and his wife, Norma, became US citizens.

Ted Forster had met me in the UK and seemed very pleased to get me on his team. At first I did an enormous amount of travelling getting to know Pentagon, US Navy and Air Force personnel and their work all over the USA. I had done some 34 states by the end of my tour. It was fortunate that we were able to fly first class. I must have stayed in hundreds of hotels and motels.

Local travel was a problem at first but one of the chaps in DRS loaned me a Hudson Hornet to start the commuting 12 miles into town from home. He charged $1 per week! Later on we bought a Pontiac for some $250. Compared with UK cars it was like an aircraft carrier. Renée had it as her car for most of the time. Later on we acquired an Austin A55 with left hand drive from the UK, brand new and then I bought a red and black Sunbeam Alpine. We took both of these British cars home on the Queen Mary in 1963.

Soon after my arrival I had to return home to my mother who was very ill with her lung cancer. We spent a week or so together at Malmo in Leopold Avenue. I went back to Washington but returned to Farnborough 2 weeks later as she had died. I stayed for her funeral and a day or two with Dad.

The various jobs in Washington produced a surprise in some respects. There had been a long inter-regnum since Beresford left and work had piled up. I found a request from myself in the UK requiring data on wide band microwave aerials! I had arrived in the USA in time to answer my own request. I found out the information, particularly from Dr. John Dyson at the University of Illinois. I got to know his family too and we still keep in touch 40 years later; in fact they visited us in the UK. I sent the data back to the RAE. I found myself involved with IFF once more. The mark had reached 12, a long cry from 1941-42 days.

Navigation systems proved to be an important aspect of my work and I did a lot of liaison in propagation work, particularly at very low frequencies.

Ted Forster liked travel and he would sometimes accompany me. He would suggest what he called a 'quickie'. That meant a trip to some six or seven places as far apart as Los Angeles Phoenix, Dallas and places in between, all in the space of about four days.

Various spheres of technical interest quickly centred onto navigation, identification and ant-submarine research. Much of the work was classified and could not be dealt with here, but the classification problem caused much delay in gaining access to almost any commercial organisation. The system of clearance despite all of our accreditations and the special relationship between the USA and UK required a significant time to elapse for everyone before a visit could be arranged.

Soon after that first Christmas in 1960, John F Kennedy was inaugurated as President of the United States of America. That particular day was very noteworthy because of a great snowfall which occurred. I drove home with a colleague, we were advised to go home at 3.30 pm. It took until about 9.30 pm to reach Ipswich Road in terrific traffic jams. Youngsters came alongside and asked for money to make a phone call home for us to advise the family of our delay. We never saw the kids again nor was there any phone call!

We had to get used to the Embassy social life. We were determined to participate in the local American domestic scene and got to know most of our neighbours very well. That first winter was traumatic. The snow lasted for six weeks. It was piled high on either side of the drive.

We joined the local church of St Luke's. Renée was assistant editor of the magazine and I was an usher (sidesman). We made many friends through the Church. Our rector had been a soldier in the Pacific in World War II, in a flame-throwing unit. He made great friends with us and he enjoyed Embassy Bourbon. He was a great advocate for Martin Luther King. Barney Ross and his family became great friends. Barney was a member of John F Kennedy's crew during the war and rescued JFK when the ship was sunk. He is featured in the film series about the life of the President. We were in the USA during nearly all of the time of the Kennedy administration.

Another very good friend was Dick Bullock with his wife, Shirley and two daughters, Carol and Jane – a strange coincidence since our own lovely daughter is called Carol Jane. Dick and I flew together once I obtained my FAA licence in 1962. He owned a Piper Tripacer and later a Mooney aircraft. I flew from Frederick Airport where Dick also kept his aircraft. Dick and Shirley came to England on our return and we flew together at Fairoaks in a Tiger Moth after that September when everything was either very flooded or wet underfoot. Dick and Shirley were stalwarts of St. Luke's Church.

We found the social and cocktail round a little tedious after a while and it was then that I started painting to while away the evenings. Embassy cheap wines and spirits could tempt the unwise, so we backed off from dinners etc. just a little. However it was usual to have a mid term and an end of tour large event. Our mid term one was done on 3 consecutive evenings. The first for US official guests, the second for Embassy friends and the third and final one for local neighbours. That last one was the noisiest. All were at Ipswich Road. The end of tour party celebrated Renée's 40th birthday. It was a glittering affair held in the Rotunda at the Embassy. Renée helped a group of ladies sponsored by Mrs Kennedy to look after deprived little coloured children in Junior Village. Carol went to Grosvenor Lane Junior School. She was very happy there. We planted a tree outside the school when we left.

Returning to work memories, there were most interesting subjects on the go. The anti-submarine detection required liaison with the US Navy. It involved even considering the effects of shoals of fish on systems. Very low frequency systems such as Omega made a very successful means of liaison. A particular good friend was Rex Stout. Satellite navigation was coming into its own and it required trips in the Baltimore direction to John Hopkins University. Telstar was the system – which was of great interest to Tom Blackband's team at Lasham back in the UK.

I attended conferences lasting a few days at a time on aerial systems. They were at a beautiful park and house near Champagne Urbana in the Illinois area south of Chicago. A character called Edwards caused a sensation by his method of retaining our attention after lunch to keep us awake. He fired a revolver with a blank cartridge!

We found the photographs taken with my Kodak Retinette camera were excellent, perhaps due to the clear atmosphere and bright sunlight.

A feature of life at the Embassy was the system of discounts available for many things including a tax exemption. One difficulty was the provision of medical aid for the US based Embassy staff. UK based people such as myself and our families were covered by British National Health provisions. Not so my secretary and others like her.

The Director General gave extramural tasks to each of us. His name was Dr. Wilson, a Scotsman. He told me to look after the Welfare Fund to assist the US based staff when in need. I cannot remember her surname, but in common with another five of the secretaries I had during my career, she was called Jean.

One day she came to me and asked if she could have a personal discussion. She wanted to know if the Welfare Fund could contribute to a new set of false teeth. The rules were that every effort should be made to find lost property before claiming from the Fund. Apparently her teeth had fallen into the toilet and disappeared. I was somewhat taken aback when she said that in order to meet the regulations, she had telephoned the sewage works to ask if they had seen her teeth! She assured me that they had not been traced and therefore could she have $90 or so for a new set! She would type my notes on return from one of my trips and could get rather alarmed if her workload increased. Mistakes and tears came easily. She eventually parted company with us when she mailed some letters in the wrong envelopes.

As to be expected, security was very tight. Each evening the security people would come around offices to check. Two misdemeanours and one could be back on the boat home. So we took turns to do our own check of our own and our colleagues' offices before leaving each evening. My neighbour Ralph Eades had a mischievous sense of humour. If he found a drawer unlocked he would draw a hammer and sickle in red on a piece of foolscap and then lock it in the drawer. The desk occupant would have fit on opening up.

He once had a signal from the Ministry in the UK asking him what he had said to an American opposite number during a discussion and in response to a statement made. He signalled back "I said oh."

We were warned one afternoon that there was to be a fire drill. When the alarm rang, Ralph set fire to a piece of paper and let the smoke drift into the air conditioning system. The staff came out of the building like rabbits out of a hole.

Upstairs the RAF staff were commanded by a Group Captain Street. He was annoyed because of the impossible workload demanded by visitors from the UK during cherry blossom time. Their numbers seemed to increase when Washington was at its most beautiful. His staff had enough work on hand without this extra load of arranging visits, security, etc. A poor view was taken by the hierarchy at home when he sent a signal saying that work would cease for several weeks 'due to the migration of the swans!'

Staff would buy right-hand drive British cars or 'Ramblers' to bring back to the UK. One of the junior female staff bought an open 2 seater white Austin Sprite. She also owned a large black Labrador dog. Cars would leave the Embassy and drive to the T-junction and traffic lights at Massachusetts Avenue during the evening rush hour. One evening I watched the American drivers stare in amazement as she drove into Massachusetts Avenue with the dog sitting bolt upright apparently driving the car because he was in the left hand seat. Many Americans could not understand that some things were different outside the United States.

We soon got in touch with Mort and Shirley Rosenhaft. Mort was billeted on my mother during the war when he was posted to RAE from the USA. He worked on weapon fuses. We were invited to dinner by Shirley to their home in Silver Spring. I was still confused by the right hand rule. We stopped at a traffic light before turning left. The approach on the left was a dual carriageway. On getting a green I turned into the left hand carriageway! I stopped realising my mistake. To my horror I was next to a stationery police car. I was dressed in a blazer and tie. I wound down the window and called to the two surprised police, "Officer have I done something wrong?" in as near an Oxford accent as I could muster. The growled reply was "Get over der" pointing a finger to the other road. Carol who was six leaned over my shoulder from the back seat and said in a loud voice, "Daddy, are we all going to prison?" Mort said later that if we had been Americans we would have been arrested.

Later during the posting a memorable trip was to California with Renée and Carol. In those days we travelled first class which delighted us. The first sight for Renée of the Grand Canyon was exciting. I recall that on the way back as we flew over it again, Carol was playing with the Air Hostess. Renée said "Carol look at the Grand Canyon", Carol replied, "I saw it on the way out."

I managed to get airborne once or twice in other than transport aircraft. The UK was very interested in an American relatively simple form of terrain following radar for the Vulcan. I went to San Diego and had a demonstration of a breadboard equipment in a WWII B26 Invader aircraft. I was positioned in the nose ahead of the pilot. We flew over the Saltan Sea, a large dried up lake, at below sea level height. We flew some 100 ft above the ground, actually below sea-level. All this was controlled by the experimental equipment. We approached a line of steep high hills. It was rather unnerving. The aircraft climbed, did an approximate stall turn right, then flew back to the lake at the previous height, all on automatics!

I had a flight in a Dakota in the P2 position up front. The pilot, a very trusting soul, let me fly it. The ailerons were heavy compared to the smaller aircraft I had experienced. Turning was very sluggish. He pattered me and let me land!.

I made several visits back home in the UK on duty to exchange information, particularly to RAE in Farnborough. This allowed me to stay at Malmo, Leopold Avenue, Farnborough, in my old wartime bedroom. During our stay in the US, we heard from Noel Strain who lived next door to Beverley Fair in Revelstoke Avenue, that the Woodcutters Cottage on the west side of our garden, was to be demolished. The cottage belonged to a Group Captain and Mrs James Leathart. They were friends of ours; James had been a Battle of Britain pilot. I contacted James and my solicitor and arranged to buy a triangle of land to fill in the gap in our hitherto L shaped garden. It was a wood. The Woodcutters area was to accommodate four blocks of four flats, garages in two blocks could be positioned along my new SW boundary. In fact in later years I had cupress trees planted to improve their area with the consent of the flat owning company. During one liaison visit I bought cupress trees to plant to hide the view from Beverley Fair towards the flats. As I write those trees are thick and as high as our house as are the trees in the Eugenie Gardens flats. On one night, 5th November, in the dark, Dad helped me to put in the new south west fence. I could only do this after work in the dark. Since it was bonfire night lots of fireworks made flashes and bangs. I said to Dad with some amusement that I felt as if we were on a wiring party during World Wars I and II.

In the third week of October 1962 I was liaising back in the UK for a few days. The Cuba crisis had started while I was away and World III seemed imminent. Renée and Carol back in Bethesda were very frightened and had gathered tinned food to place in the basement in case a nuclear war was beginning. The UK did not seem to be very alarmed. One evening at the height of the crisis, I was with several British and some five or six American officers in uniform. We listened to the radio news. As the US National Anthem was played, the US officers stood to attention with the right hands on their hearts. It seemed an odd stance to the British.

I came home twice by air of course to attend promotion boards in London. I didn't get the first one, probably due to jet lag and travel delays caused by a US internal airways strike. I had to travel to New York from Washington by train. A liaison officer (RAF) collected me in New York at 5.00 am and I flew with RAF transport command to UK, in a VC10 (sitting backwards). I had a senior officer position which was indistinguishable from the others. I did the trip again a few months later and succeeded in being promoted to PSO.

One trip to the UK using RAF transport many years later was flown with the passenger list including an American General and his wife. My better seat had to be given up to these special guests. Unfortunately I had to travel on crutches this time due to having trapped my sciatic nerve. I could not have a car to the terminal at Brize Norton, I had to struggle onto a bus which hurt. More of that stay later.

Renée's 40th birthday on 12th August 1963 had to be special. A party was arranged for lots of friends in the Rotunda at the British Embassy. It was a wonderful affair with a fantastic spread of food and drinks with waiters and servers. Renée loved it.

When she returned to England, Renée drove the Austin with its left hand drive. She had driven her Pontiac in the USA with no problems. She failed the UK driving test to her and my surprise. After getting some tuition which the instructor said wasn't needed because she was a good driver, Renée decided the problem was the left hand drive. So before the third test she told the examiner that he would probably be a bit scared sitting on the wrong side, so she passed and never looked back. Renée was a good driver but like all ladies found that hard to believe.

America changed Renée's outlook on the future and immediately upon her return to the UK, she went to the technical colleges in Camberley and Farnborough and took A levels in Sociology, English and English Literature also she became a wonderful potter. Her gift in the latter is evidenced in her pottery ware at home and listed in the catalogue I made for Carol, in fact Renée wrote a thesis on Byzantine pottery. The catalogue has listed all of these items which we would like kept within the family or at least within family ownership.

Chapter 8

AMERICAN HOLIDAYS

Several holidays in the USA and Canada were special. One which sticks in the memory was the voyage on a ship, the SS Evangeline, from Washington DC to Bermuda. We sailed down the Potomac River out into the Atlantic. Although by large cruiser liner standards the Evangeline was small, it was comfortable and well crewed. Bermuda was all that we had hoped. Little did I realise, at the time, that upon my return to RAE I would go there frequently on duty. The narrow roads with its mopeds as the main traffic, and our visit with bathing at Pink Beach were another world to us after the Washington environment.

Before leaving the island we were returning to the ship after a day ashore. We were passing a park bounded with an iron-railing fence. A memorial to the British Army interested me and we stopped to look. Carol stuck her head through the railings to get a better view. Fine, but she got her head stuck and could not get away. As Renée and I began to panic, the ship, which was some 200 yards away sounded its siren, calling all passengers to board immediately. As we struggled her yells could be heard by all nearby. With Renée pulling on Carol and with me trying to bend the iron bars we had a vision of being left behind. We eventually got a very unhappy girl free and we ran for the ship. We boarded last, just in time with a lasting memory of the island.

We were very keen to explore the deep south of the USA, and to do it in a different way to our normal mode of air travel. We planned to visit New Orleans and to travel by train from Washington. It came as a bit of a shock to learn that it meant overnight sleeper car accommodation since the trip would take a couple of days. The train was reasonable but quite slow. We were introduced at breakfast to the US serving of grits, a sort of porridge which we found difficult to swallow. It seemed so different to the other extreme of pancakes, sausages and jam on the same plate.

New Orleans, particularly the old quarter, lived up to its name with jazz bands in many of the bars. Carol could not come with us in the evening so Renée looked after her while I listened to the bands. I well recall the acquisition of a new taste for oysters which could be bought over the bar.

When I took leave of absence from the Embassy, Ted Forster insisted on a telephone contact number in case of problems back at work. He would, much to Renée's annoyance get me to phone in periodically.

While in New Orleans I was told that I was needed urgently at a meeting with the US people back in Washington. We had to cut our holiday short, catch the train and return. I attended the meeting and to my disgust found that there was nothing for me to say!

I mentioned earlier that we flew to California and saw the Grand Canyon from the air. We began that trip from Baltimore in deep snow. We arrived in Los Angeles in hot sunshine which set the scene for a memorable visit. I combined official work with the holiday and we booked in at the El Cortez Hotel in San Diego. The position of the hotel overlooked the airport from a hill just south of the runway. From our room we could see aircraft on short final approach level with our window and only a couple of hundred yards away.

San Diego Zoo attracted Renée and Carol but the spectacular sight was the US Navy ships in the harbour. We visited the Mexican border. I had been to Mexico but Renée had not and she looked wistfully at the other side before we set off for Santa Barbara and San Francisco.

I had shown Renée and Carol photographic slides of Santa Barbara prior to our visit to California. I had taken them on earlier duties. When she saw the real thing I was told that despite the beauty of the buildings I had not photographed all the dustbins and other rubbish which gave a slight downgrading of the various scenes.

While in Los Angeles we visited a friend, Gladys Du Common in her lovely house at San Marino near Pasadena. She was mother of California at the time and a great sponsor of the Huntington Park Library. We visited the lovely park and the art gallery in the library. I was sad in a way from an English point of view to find paintings there by Gainsborough and other of our famous artists. 'Pinky' and 'Blue Boy' are there. Such beautiful paintings maybe should be at home in the UK.

San Francisco provided the wonderful tram rides, Top of the Mark hotel for drinks and a fantastic view and the essential visit of Fisherman's Wharf. The most impressive day however was spent in the ride over the Golden Gate Bridge and the sight of the Sequoia Pines, some 200 ft high they took one's breath away.

An eagerly awaited holiday was to Canada. I drove the Austin A55 some 600 miles to get there. We cheered as we crossed Rainbow Bridge and saw the Union Jack, which formed part of the Canadian flag at that time. We arrived in Ontario and visited the mother of our neighbour Dr Noel Strain back in Farnborough. The sight of Niagara Falls was impressive as was a sail around the Thousand Islands although mosquitoes and midges were a nuisance.

Quebec provided the chance of visiting the Heights of Abraham where General Wolfe had fought the French and won. Wolfe had been the Commander at one time of the 15th of Foot Regiment, which became the East Yorkshire Regiment. Each year Quebec Day was celebrated by all ranks in the Regiment by the wearing of white rose of Yorkshire. I brought home a stone from the site.

We were very impressed by Old Fort Henry. This fort or barracks was in excellent condition and was manned by soldiers of the British Army of the 1870s. They were actually students but behaved exactly as those

xxxi - The guard on parade at Old Fort Henry, Kingston, Ontario.

soldiers of a century earlier. The illustrations give a flavour of the sight. If only Victoria Barracks could have been dealt with before its demolition in the way Old Fort Henry was attracting so many tourists.

The drive home was exhausting. I did the 600 miles in one day, I cannot recall why it was so important to get back to Bethesda so quickly.

1962-1963 was the Centenary of the American Civil War. We attended a re-enactment of the Battle of Menassis. It was extremely well done but spoilt by the theft of a cine camera I had borrowed from Mort for the occasion.

I also went with Dick Bullock to the Gettysburg battlefield. I was surprised to find the positions of every regiment marked along the lines. The few hundred yards separating each side was reminiscent of those distances I saw at the Aldershot Tattoo as a boy.

Chapter 9

RETURN TO THE ROYAL AIRCRAFT ESTABLISHMENT AND HOME

Carol was most unhappy to leave Ipswich Road, Bethesda, Maryland. She left school and Renée and I donated and planted the tree in the school grounds (I think it was a cherry tree) in memory of Carol's attendance at the Grosvenor Lane School and our stay as a family in the USA. We, and especially Renée, worked so very hard to make the house clean and tidy before we left. She was wiping the floor behind her as she moved towards the door.

We drove in convoy to New York, Renée driving the Austin 1500 behind me with Carol in my Sunbeam Alpine. She was marvellous, Renée that is. She only once let someone get between the two cars, a lorry and that for only a short time. It was an exhausting trip for her. When we got to the motel prior to boarding the Queen Mary for our return to England, she fell into my arms crying with exhaustion and relaxation of considerable tension. She was magnificent. After a very good trip back, with a first class cabin and second class dining room with fantastic food, we drove in convoy again to Farnborough and this time on the left hand side of the road. Again, Renée was magnificent.

We soon settled back into Beverley Fair and got Carol into the newly located St Peter's School. She had to pass her 11 plus within a year or so of our return i.e. August 1963 and she had enjoyed her days in America, but the educational standard for 9-10 year olds was not up to the UK level. We therefore had to arrange a tutor, one of her teachers, to give her extra coaching.

Before we came home I had made a liaison visit to RAE to seek a post on my return. I met John Mills, Head of Radio Department and he offered me the choice of two projects, either to set up and run a team to research and develop a comprehensive long range aircraft navigation system or to work on anti-submarine sonobuoy research. I chose the former project which, in retrospect, was probably most fortunate. He said that I would start from scratch with no staff or even an office. I had to build everything up.

Within a few weeks I had managed accommodation in R16 Building and enlisted a team which gradually grew with much emphasis upon the Omega Very Low Frequency Navigation System being evolved and its integration with the Inertial Navigation (IN) and other systems. The IN side was under the control of the Flight Systems Department, Margaret Treadgold and 'Robby' Robinson. Our side involved a lot of work on propagation.. My team was part of the Navigation Division, headed by Steve Jones who proved to be a great friend. I soon managed to acquire the use of the Comet III flying laboratory which was used for many long range flights. This narrative may not be in exact order of time sequence but I am writing items as they come to mind. I wrote many papers and devised new schemes including work upon the use of Differential Omega. I had many battles with the CAA representatives who did not believe that Omega would be successful – only Inertial Navigation held promise. History has proved them wrong and 30 years later Omega was still fitted to many aircraft. Fortunately I had some very bright people in my team, Ray Couzens and John Lawson come to mind.

I had an Auster Mk IX available to me for personal experiments with a cheap Omega system. I had a good assistant to help me while the big stuff was produced by Ray and the others. We did many flights abroad endeavouring to find a solution to the vagaries of the ionosphere D layer propagation problems and the slipping of Omega Hyperbolic Lanes.

Many friendships with Radio Flight and Southern Squadron pilots and navigators were established during the work. Harry Shaw, navigator and private pilot (came 2nd in the UK – Australia Race as co-pilot and owned a Hornet Moth G.A.E.S.E and Fournier RF4) became a very close friend. He was a superb navigator.

The various types of equipment needed for the examination of Omega and the integration of it with Inertial Navigation and other systems was built and installed in the Comet III. This aircraft was unique in that although it was fitted with four engines, each pair were of different type.

Since the whole object was to produce a long range system we needed to fly long range, hence flights were made across the Atlantic to Newfoundland, Barbados and elsewhere. Many trips were made to Barbados where, usually we took over the Bagshot House Hotel, in Worthing. This beautiful place was right on the beach and run by Mrs Robinson and her daughter. Usually we travelled as three distinct units, the aircrew, the boffins and the ground crew, since we needed to ensure proper servicing of our unique flying laboratory.

There were several very amusing occasions during our various overseas flights. We were divided essentially into the three groups, the aircrew, the boffins and the ground crew. Friendly rivalry, particularly before dinner in the evening involved filling drawers in a bedroom with land crabs and squirting a hosepipe through the window.

I had a hard time consoling the aircrew when two of my team would not put their duty free booze into the kitty to entertain guests of ours at a Barbados party. The two men concerned wondered why they were not on the overseas team again!

We had parties at the hotel for many guests including the Governor (before independence) his wife, and the Prime Minister of Barbados, who happened to be a Liveryman of the Guild of Air Pilots and Air Navigators.

Barbados was wonderful, children and young men would play cricket on the beach and even on the roads after dark. One memorable visit was the occasion when the Experimental Flying Department RAE Officer Commanding, Group Captain Peter Thorne came out with us. He did much to add flavour to the trip and every time I meet him years later he refers to it.

Peter and I received an invitation to the Governor's at Government House for lunch followed by a visit to the races. We went by taxi and were received in right royal fashion. Lunch was attended by about half a dozen waiters just for the four of us. Her Ladyship was not present. She told me afterwards at a party that protocol demanded that she should stay in her room upstairs; she had sandwiches. We departed for the races in a limousine driven by a soldier in white uniform. The uniformed, pith helmeted, guard presented arms as we passed the gate.

Upon arrival at the race course we entered the Royal Box. All stood for the National Anthem, upon arrival of the Governor. When we sat down he placed his nice hat on a little table in front of him and invited me to do the same. My hat was a straw porkpie type which cost $1 in Miami. It had a small hole from wear in the front crown; I used it for swimming in the sea to avoid sunburn. I still have that hat and never forget when it shared the table with the hat of the Governor of Barbados in the Royal Box. Peter and I did quite well with the race betting, but His Excellency didn't. The last race included a horse called 'Ad Astra'. Since the Royal Air Force motto is 'Per Adua Ad Astra', Peter and I backed it and it won! But H.E. didn't which made him more fed up, a gin & tonic back home cheered him up and Peter and I went back to Bagshot House after a very good day.

Peter made quite an impression upon Mrs Robinson and her daughter. Upon leaving the hotel for the airport and our trip home in the Comet, he arranged for me to get the three hired cars (for which I was responsible) to contain, respectively, the aircrew, the boffins and the ground crew. The latter had to back out first into the narrow road, followed by myself and my team, then the aircrew. This meant they would lead the convoy and it allowed Peter, resplendent in tropical uniform, to be the last to say farewell to our hosts. With a nonchalant wave of his hand, he reversed over the road and backed into the opposite stone wall! The car was dented. He said on arrival at the airport, "fix it with the car firm, Freddy!!" They were not pleased. I raced to the aircraft and with engines running we were hauled aboard.

We left during a sunny morning, unlike the night flight on one occasion when the runway and airfield lights all failed just as we were accelerating for take-off. We pressed on into a dark void. Our return with Peter was quite remarkable. I had stressed to the ground crew that on no account should they try to smuggle any liquor into the UK. During the flight, Peter, who was supernumerary and had nothing to do, wandered round the Comet and smelt rum. He opened the water container and found it full of the stuff. In chastising the culprits, said that those not working, i.e. the ground crew and himself should drink it before landing; things got rather jolly. Arrival in the UK was interesting since Peter's beloved wife, Mary, had come to welcome him home. A customs man came aboard, smelt rum and looked in the container. He turned to an inebriated ground crewman and asked him what it was, his reply was "Itsh the unconshumed portion of the daily rashuns."

On one of the Omega flights on the way from Newfoundland to Barbados, while making test communications with Cove Radio Station near Farnborough on single sideband HF radio, we received a message for Ray Couzens, my 2i/c from, his wife. The message indicated a price offered for the sale of his house – should she sell? After some consideration he agreed and the reply was duly acted upon.

While in Barbados on one occasion we all went to a Barbeque with a West Indian steel band playing. We met two girls whose father was David Bargman and an old 6th form school friend of mine. We had done Engineering Drawing together and he was RQMs of the Cadets. He lived with his parents in a house near the Clockhouse at Farnborough where the glass GPO building now stands. His father had built a beautiful 6ft long model destroyer in a glass case. David had apparently become a Meteorological Officer in Africa. The girls invited us back to their flat and private beach for a night-time swim. I have never known so many people get into a Mini. On arrival at the flat we were greeted by a very fierce Alsatian. We got into our swim trunks and all went down to the sea. While all floating in a circle feet to feet looking up at the stars, someone said that at night sharks would sometimes get over the coral reef and swim into the lagoon. Being an abject coward I made rapid tracks for the beach only to be greeted by the Alsatian which did not let me out of the water. I had to plead for assistance from his owner to make a safe retreat and dry off.

We did a lot of trips to Bermuda where my original visit was with Renée and Carol when we made the cruise in the SS Evangeline from Washington. The official visits from Farnborough as part of the radio wave VLF propagation research resulted in people such as Bill Langrish staying there monitoring transmissions for a month on one occasion. While water skiing he managed to get himself badly stung by jellyfish.

While in Barbados I was looked after by a native lady called Dolly. She let me photograph her on the beach just outside the Bagshot House Hotel dining room. I painted a picture of the scene; it now hangs over our staircase at Beverley Fair.

We had a signal from our Division Leader Johnny Johnson one day, insisting that we return immediately to the UK because the Comet was required for another urgent job. We had only one more night flight to do in and out of Barbados to complete the series. I sent a return signal saying that we would return immediately, but I timed the take-off to allow us to complete our one more trial. The signal was sent, with full knowledge of

xxxii - Comet 3 XN453, our flying laboratory.

the time difference, to arrive after RAE had closed. By the time the signal was read in the UK we had done our trip and set off home.

A very exciting night flight involved a return to the UK from Barbados via Santa Maria airfield in the Azores. The navigation equipment, used by Harry Shaw our Navigator, packed up. It was getting foggy at our destination and fuel was not enough to go elsewhere. Harry, by miraculous dead reckoning navigation, got us to Santa Maria. A small island in a large ocean. He got news of his promotion to Squadron Leader while at the VOQ (Visiting Officers Quarters) swimming pool in the Azores. We used to hear the tune "A Walk in the Black Forest" on the jukebox till we were sick of it. The chaps found a woman there who wanted to dance to it. We would select one unfortunate member of the team to be a gentleman. It was a real bind. She was so unlovely that we referred to her as Victor Mature.

We made trips to the Federal Aviation Authority in the USA to describe our Omega work. Pictures in the family album show me making one of the presentations.

I also attended several conferences, some overseas at symposia generated by the Royal Institute of Navigation and its German or French counterparts. I sometimes gave a paper. While in Miami, John Young, an ex Battle of Britain pilot and old friend persuaded me to join the Guild of Air Pilots and Air Navigators. From that occasion I graduated from about 1964 to Master of the Guild in 1989 with Renée as the First Lady or Mistress of the Guild as she enjoyed, saying that she was Mistress to 1500 pilots.

My round the world trip with Renée to visit the Guild branches in Hong Kong, Australia and New Zealand was a highlight of our times together. The RAF took good care of us in Hong Kong and our stay in the Peninsula

xxxiii - VHF Omega Presentation to the FAA of the Comet trial results. Washington DC, 1969. (Crown Copyright MoD)

Hotel gave us a feel for almost pre-war times. The visit to Brisbane was memorable in that the Governor invited us to stay in Government House. Renée had a suite, maid and butler, just previously enjoyed by Princess Diana when she visited Australia with the Prince of Wales.

I was invited to give the Sylvanus P Thompson Series of Lectures to various universities throughout the UK and in Dublin. Each lecture was followed by a dinner chaired by the Vice Chancellor. In every case except one, the wives of the senior university staff attended the dinner but not the talk. The exception was Dublin. During the meal the head waiter whispered to my host alongside me that the ladies had arrived with their cars to take the staff home. My host replied, "give them a stout and tell them to wait!" I had some barracking from one or two Aer Lingus aircrew during my talk there.

A very different overseas exercise was unique. The Comet was routed to Lebanon. We flew to Beirut and were surprised on landing to find anti-aircraft guns positioned on either side of the runway. After two days' stay including bathing in the Mediterranean we assembled for departure. Firstly we found that our very popular navigator, Flt. Lt. Leo Rowe was very ill with a tummy bug and in need of treatment by a service doctor in Malta, our next stop.

We were taken aback when we learned that the Lebanese authorities would not let us go until we had paid for the aircraft fuel in cash! A very long argument followed. Our aircrew gradually talked them into accepting promises to arrange for the money to arrive by the usual channels.

Freddy Stringer

xxxv - RAE circa 1969. (Crown Copyright MoD)

xxxiva - Exercise 'Canopus' round the world trip in Comet 4, Boscombe Down.

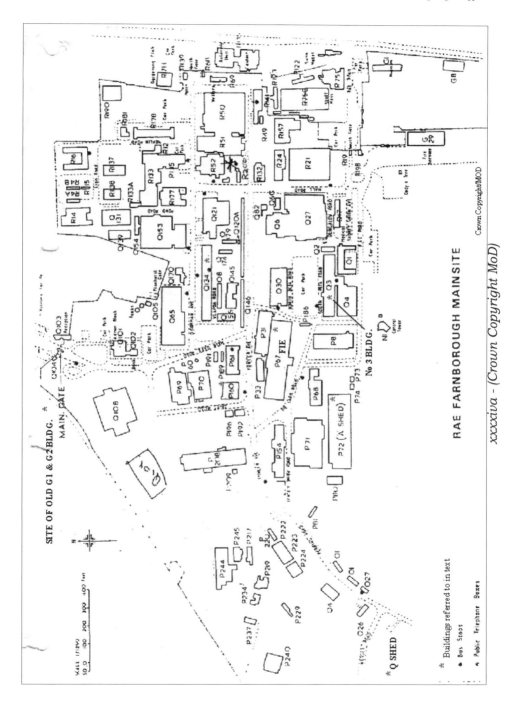

SITE OF OLD G1 & G2 BLDG. *

MAIN GATE

No 3 BLDG.

RAE FARNBOROUGH MAIN SITE

Crown Copyright/MOD

xxxxiva - (Crown Copyright MoD)

* Buildings referred to in text
• Bus Stops
✦ Public Telephone Boxes

* Q SHED

The Institution of Electrical Engineers
South West Scotland Graduate and Student Section.

THE SILVANUS P. THOMPSON LECTURE
for Graduates and Students

ELECTRONICS — ITS FUTURE IN NAVIGATION

by F. S. Stringer, B.Sc., F.Inst (Nav), A.F.R.Ae.S.

Room M406, The University of Strathclyde
Montrose Street, Glasgow.

Tuesday, 26th January 1971 at 7.30 p.m.

SYNOPSIS

The tools at the disposal of operatives and problems of introducing them.

The problems of navigation and the need, if any, for improvement.

Pilot navigation and seaways.

The improvement to navigation provided by modern technology.

Extensions to existing approach and landing systems to accommodate more traffic.

Cost effectiveness problems and present investment.

The A T C problem, VTOL, STOL and SST.

Admission by ticket available from

I. C. Buchanan
12 Cromarty Avenue
Newlands
Glasgow S.3.

xxxvi

Chapter 10

THE POSTING TO THE MINISTRY OF DEFENCE – 1970

I applied two or three times for jobs as an Assistant Director (Senior Principal Scientific Officer) at MOD. The first of these was not in London, but at RAE Bedford, dealing with the automatic landing of aircraft. I didn't get that job; it was won by Geoff Howell who later became Head of Flight Systems Department and subsequently Chief Scientist at the Civil Aviation Agency.

The second job was with the Directorate of Navigation, MOD. The post was Assistant Director (AD) Nav4 under Bill Broughton as Director; the father of Group Captain David Broughton who is presently Director of The Royal Institute of Navigation. The office was in St Giles Court near Tottenham Court Road Station – a building that Carol our daughter likened to a prison. I attended the interview and it seemed to go reasonably well. I also later applied for an AD post for the Multi Role Combat Aircraft (MRCA) aircraft, later known as the Tornado and the backbone of the RAF. I duly attended the interview but I had the strange experience of having the Chairman leaving part way through the proceedings, saying he had to be elsewhere. The exercise went on in standard fashion but I felt all was not well. I realised why the fiasco had occurred later when it was published that I had been awarded the AD Nav4 job. This news had been confidential (Staff in Confidence) before the MRCA interview. I did not know it, but the MRCA board knew.

I was somewhat disappointed by my standing at D Nav, Bill Broughton was my Director, he was a very kind man. However my particular role seemed under the influence of AD Nav2, John McIvor. Nav1 was mostly equipment generally for the RAF; Nav2 was civil equipment and I think it was Nav3 under Ron Fish dealing with MRCA which became the Tornado. Ron died some time later.

I was involved with such things as the trials and tribulations of dealing with the CAA and airlines in getting the Trident airliner through its Category III complete autoland trials. I was not very happy really although authorisation was completed eventually. Transfer to the newly formed Jim Briggs Directorate at the Adelphi, Strand circa 1972 made a complete change. I was surprised to be asked to move but I became ADXR3 – Assistant Director Extramural Research – with a wide responsibility for Avionics research programmes with industry. At one time my budget was £16M per annum! It was amusing how that figure was reached. I was asked by Jim Briggs to decide the amount needed to meet each section of Major Field 14, I decided the figure while I was in the bath. It was accepted. All subsequent figures and increases were based on those bathtime 'thoughts'.

I was fortunate enough to have two RAF Squadron Leaders on my staff in Adelphi. Each was very memorable. The first was Ken Clark and the second was Mike Stretton, Ken was such fun. When abroad on AGARD trips, his humour made sometimes boring meetings very amusing. Back at Adelphi he was also amused by the occasion when my secretary, another Jean, called me on my office phone to enquire about the cups of tea for some RAF officers visiting me from MOD. She said, "Do they all take milk, Mr Sugar?" Ken was amused when he found me talking to two pigeons on the windowsill. By the open window he heard me say, "Just how do you buggers navigate?"

Mike Stretton was a very energetic Lightning fighter pilot. I always found that a current serving officer would bring sense operationally into whatever research programme was involved. One day in Adelphi, two Wing Commanders from MOD in Whitehall wanted to visit my office to discuss a new idea they had. Mike heard that they were coming and asked me if he could join the meeting. I did not agree and said that the discussion was just for me to listen to their proposals. Mike pressed me again and again. Eventually I told him that he could come to the meeting on two conditions. Firstly, that he did not speak, secondly that he took notes. The visitors duly arrived and Mike took the seat I had for him alongside me. The visitors began their detailed description of the piece of research they thought would increase the RAF combat capability. Mike had stayed silent for some time but I then felt a dig in the ribs from behind, but I ignored it. After a second dig I whispered to Mike, what do you want. He said "May I speak, Sir?" I said "No". After a third dig, I said "OK but keep it short". Mike said "Thank you", then in a positive tone, said "Balls".

My view from my fifth floor office window was tremendous. I could see the Thames up to the Houses of Parliament and much in between. During the six years I was in London the IRA were very active. One day after a loud explosion I saw a pillar of smoke rise from where a bomb had exploded a few hundred yards away.

I found the electric lighting in the office very poor. I asked for a reading lamp. A man arrived and measured the level of light with the overhead arrangement switched on. He declared that the readings showed it to be sufficient and therefore despite being an Assistant Director I did not merit a reading lamp. This was too much, so I brought a lamp from home, I was then told it was illegal because of regulations. So I started to complain officially once more. The administration relented but insisted that an issue reading lamp must be connected and tested by an official electrician. This was done. I was told also that if a bulb needed changing I must not do it myself, but must send for the man who could – officially.

I was selected while at MOD to become a member of the UK team on AGARD. This was part of NATO and is the Aerospace Group for Advisory Research and Development. I became the UK representative for avionics.

Many symposia were held in all of the countries of the NATO alliance. A lot of preparation was needed and many papers were presented to share advanced technology. Some were classified, others were not.

I travelled a lot, to USA, Canada and many European countries. Eventually I persuaded Renée to come with me to the European venues. She probably enjoyed Portugal, Greece and Denmark, especially Portugal where she did a lot of visits to sites of interest. The visits to Italy and Greece produced some very interesting events.

One occasion in Marathon in Greece was one in which I was the Conference Chairman. I carefully briefed all the Session Chairman on the question of timing. Each Chairman had to give the speaker a three-minute warning and then stop the speaker as his allotted time ran out. On the particular day the Chairman fell asleep, I woke him up and got more excited as he let the speaker drone on. In sheer frustration I got up then moved up the aisle to find the power switch and turn off the slide projector. I was unaware of a thunderstorm going on outside. As I approached the projector, a local electrical sub-station was struck by lightening. All the lights went out. A colleague said "I knew that you were a Churchwarden, but I hadn't realised how you had contacts with the Almighty to that degree!!"

A meeting in Turkey was set up in Ankara, surprisingly during a period of civil unrest. On return awaiting the boarding of a Turkish Airlines aircraft we were surrounded by a lot of soldiers in the airport terminal. I was called over the public address system to report back to the departure desk. Fearing trouble I was relieved to learn that it was only for checking a minor detail. However as we walked from the terminal to the aircraft we had to negotiate a line of soldiers with machine guns on either side of our path. During the flight I saw a man and a young woman walking round the aircraft making notes. When they got to me I asked what they were doing. They said, "We are doing the aircraft inspection!"

Probably the largest project to involve me directly as the AD in avionics was 'Fly by wire', culminating in the FBW Jaguar. Theoretical work and much basic research had been done by the Flight Systems Department at RAE in Farnborough and Bedford. The technique involved the control of the combat aircraft by electrical signals from the control column, rudder, throttle, etc. to the aerodynamic control surface by electrical signals rather than control rods. The whole system was operated by a complex computer system. The mechanical movement of the controls requires servo units to convert the electrical signals into mechanical force. For safety reasons it was essential that total computer failure would be a few parts in one to ten million or so. A very tall order. Much of the debate centred around the triplex or quadruplex computer multiplication. With British Aerospace at Warton in Lancashire involved in the practical design and installation of a fly by wire system in a Jaguar aircraft, I found myself flying up there with the help of RAE Transport Flight on many occasions.

The project involved a lot of financial support from my budget, in fact a major part of it. I had to decide if a single seat or dual seat Jaguar would be used for the work. I decided, against the wishes of some at RAE, that it should be a single seat aircraft. One thought at the back of my mind was that the inclusion of a scientific observer would trigger recommendations of refinements to the design. This would increase time scales and costs. In the event the single seat option went ahead.

When the installation was ready for flight, I had the tremendous task of getting authority for the aircraft to fly. No aircraft had ever used controls with no mechanical reversion to the flying control surfaces. I tried for some time before I got the required signature from the appropriate Director. One of my arguments was that if instead the Wright Brothers had not made the first powered flight in 1903, but had tried to fly in the 1970s, and if authority did not approve, the aviation world would have been set back possibly for decades.

In 1976 it was decided by the MOD Procurement Executive that my part of the London scene should be lodged at RAE Farnborough. I soon returned to my old Establishment, this time to the Flight Systems Department. Instead of being AD/SRA3, I became ADXR/FS, where FS was the Department, not my initials.

Chapter 11

RETURN TO RAE AGAIN

I returned in 1976 to Farnborough as the ADXR Flight Systems Department (Assistant Director Extramural Research). I was blessed with another secretary called Jean, this time Jean Morgan. She was superb, a lovely lady who worked hard and made life easier for me. She was a local girl whose father had owned a butcher shop in Victoria Road, Farnborough.

The work was similar to that I had been used to in London. However, as part of an RAE Department the interests of the local teams figured high in my sights.

The new surroundings and the exciting projects made me keen to return to the actual research and development itself, rather than arrange work with industry. I was given a new division concerned with flight instruments. This soon became the Cockpit Research Division – Geoff Hunt took on the job of ADXR.

The projects were very forward looking. Night Vision Goggles (NVG), Head Up Displays, the management of helicopter systems for military operations, the conversion of analogue displays to digital alphanumeric types was just some of the work. The Night Vision Goggle programme involved the use of experimental items. In 1981 the advent of The Falk-

xxxvii - The Division, 1981.

xxxviii - The Sea King and team with Jean Morgan centre and me on the right, 1981. (Crown Copyright/MoD)

land Island war provided a decisive change in the status and the speed of decision-making. The experimental units were used operationally.

When the Falklands situation became an operational issue, I had a meeting in my home on the Sunday morning with my senior staff, particularly my RAF officer. We wondered what part we could play to ease the task of the Armed Services. It was agreed that our experimental NVGs could play a useful role. The snag was that our models were loaned and some were as far afield as Malvern. I arranged to drive half way there and meet my opposite number from RSRE and bring the items back to Farnborough. We got them all back and John Denyer on my staff at the time was able to teach RAF and other personnel to use them. For this he had to fly to the Azores. John was awarded the John Dickenson medal by the Guild of Air Pilots and Air Navigators. He is, at the time of writing, the Director of Boscombe Down.

I had the occasional reasons to visit the USA after my tour at the British Embassy. While in the Defence Research Staff we had formed a great friendship with the Bullock family. Dick Bullock owned a Tripacer aircraft which we flew together from Frederick, Maryland.

On one of my return visits I landed in a commercial aircraft at Washington National Airport about 9.00 pm. It was 2.00 am back in the UK. Dick met me at the airport and said that he had cancelled my hotel booking and that I would be staying with the Bullock family, back in Bethesda, Maryland. Despite my desperate need to get to bed, he said that his new Mooney aircraft had some new avionics and he wanted me

xxxix - HRH and the Director see the Model Terrain for the Attack Simulator. (Crown Copyright MoD)

to see it, there and then. We motored out to Dulles International Airport where the Mooney was based. We took off into the night and flew north climbing to several thousand feet. Having shown me the gear in operation we turned back and called Dulles. They gave us a new altimeter pressure setting. As Dick adjusted the pressure, both needles fell off their pivots and landed in the bottom of the instrument rendering it useless. We told Dulles of our problem. They gave us a final approach clearance to the left hand runway. We dropped the undercarriage and flaps and made a long approach from several thousand feet. We landed safely but it made our eyes water. I could never expect a UK major airport giving such priority to a small private aircraft.

Once again I was able to ensure that a current Squadron Leader fighter pilot was on the Staff. I had another Lightning pilot also a Wing Commander and a Lt. Colonel liaison officer with each of the appropriate services attached.

Simulation became an important aspect of the work of my Division. The Division had a combat simulator which allowed us to insert the flight profiles of two aircraft in air combat. The friendly aircraft was the simulated cockpit equipped with our various displays and the other was the enemy which appeared on a virtual reality display outside. The RAF pilot was used to test the various displays. We always wanted to insert the friendly aircraft as a Sopwith Camel of World War I and the enemy as a Fokker D VIII, but we never got round to it.

For low level operations the display was generated by a small camera which traversed a huge model landscape at the appropriate scale altitude. The model was the size of a wall in a large room. The illustration here shows the model being demonstrated to a member of the Royal Family by our Deputy Director at the time, later Director, Geoffrey Pope.

Chapter 12

FLYING INSTRUCTOR AND EXAMINER

During 1943 I remember Sgt. Doug Houslay flying a Tiger Moth for construction training, and I had longed to join him. 26 years later I was there to be examined in such an aircraft as an Assistant Instructor. I had to wait over a quarter of a century to satisfy my wish at Biggin Hill in 1969.

My first training job part-time unpaid was at White Waltham. Peter Coyle and I both got the job teaching the Metropolitan Police Flying Club in a Colt aircraft. I had to get an endorsement by Sid Parker to instruct in the Colt with a test at Fairoaks sitting in the right hand seat. I had flown many hours in the Colt with my father at Fairoaks but it was interesting flying from the right. Strangely in 2003 I feel strange sitting the left hand seat having spent some 2860 hours on the right.

The White Waltham experience was very valuable. The airfield operations were controlled by the RAF; a university Air Squadron shared the airfield with the primary club viz, the West London Aero Club (WLAC).

There were many interesting instances during this first time with WLAC; I joined the club and became a member of four; the RAE Aero Club, Fairoaks, Thruxton and WLAC, all at the same time.

I have two favourite memories of that time. Firstly there was the policewoman called Josie, she was very good and got her licence easily. She later left the police and became an instructor, then flew twin engine aircraft delivering heart organs around the country.

The second memory is of a Scotland Yard Inspector who found the circuit exercise workload very high. He tended to fixate on one thing in the circuit. On one occasion flying on runway 25, as we turned on to left base leg, he began the descent without pause at 500ft. Back gardens and washing lines came into view so I took control and landed. When I asked him why had he not turned onto the runway heading to land, he said, "I know I had to turn four corners, I must have missed one!!"

During my time as Master of the Guild of Air Pilots and Air Navigators (1989-90), I was pleased to welcome Prince Philip as Grand Master to a Livery Dinner. I told him the story about the 'four corners' flight. He found it hard to believe.

The Metropolitan Police Flying Club CFI was a Sergeant. We could not spin the Piper Colt so spinning had to be done at Blackbushe in a Beagle Pup. My first student to do this asked me how the Pup behaved in and out of a spin. I said I didn't know as I hadn't done one in it before. An early Pup I believe had a problem in an overseas occasion when the wing collapsed on recovery; too much G I expect.

In 1971 the Police Club decided to move to Denham and fly a Cessna 152. I continued with them for a while but found the journey too long and not so enjoyable in the 152 as the Colt. The 152 did not have a good climb rate with flap after a 'go around'. High tension cables in the overshoot didn't help. The Police Club moved subsequently to Biggin Hill so I moved to Blackbushe in September 1971 for a time flying an Australian aircraft – The Airtourer with a small club. One or two outstanding flights are worth recording.

I was given an Indian student one Saturday afternoon. He had reached the stage of his introduction to the circuit pattern, take-off and landing. He wanted to learn to fly quickly so that he could join the Indian Air Force to fight Pakistan. There was a war between the two countries at the time. We took off with my demonstrating and pattering with the student. The circuit at Blackbushe was crowded that afternoon. As we reached late down-wind, Air Traffic Control advised me that we were number four to land. Later ATC said that there were parachutists landing to the north of the runway. Since my student had not landed an aircraft previously, I said "I have control". He replied, "No, I have control". I repeated my instruction, whereupon he tried to wrestle the controls from me. I managed to get the Victor Airtourer on the ground safely and taxied back to dispersal. I went to the CFI and said I would not continue the exercise with the student, nor would I fly with him again.

One damp and dismal wet afternoon at Blackbushe, I was taking off on runway 18 when to my surprise we passed a lady pushing a pram coming towards us on the left hand side of the runway!

I left the Blackbushe Club and continued flying at Redhill and did more general part-time instruction at White Waltham. As a check pilot with the Tiger Club at Redhill, I had an all types rating and I tested new members and did check flights in addition to enjoying such aircraft as CDC, the oldest Tiger Moth, the Stampes, Fox Moth and others. Some of the Fox Moth flying was at Rochester. I flew there from Farnborough in our Chipmunk G.BDDD and sometimes used it to visit Marconi GEC on duty. I actually managed to be paid car rate for the journey after lengthy discussion with the travel claims people at RAE.

I continued to instruct the RAE Flying Club – formed originally in 1922. The aircraft originally was a Tiger Moth G-AJHS but later it was the Piper Cherokee Challenger PA 28-180 Registration G-BBKX. I am still flying it at the time of writing. Also at the RAE Club is the DH Chipmunk G-BDDD.

For several years while the Aero Club was based in 'Q shed at RAE, a CAPIOb aircraft was loaned to us by James Black, a very expert aerobatic pilot. He had excelled in the Tiger Club and currently owns 'Charlie Zulu' and Russian aircraft; also Tiger Moths for interest flights for the public. Charlie Zulu became my favourite aircraft. It is delightful to fly and is very manoeuvrable.

On 15 April 1985 during the time that the Civil Enclave was being formed, I was asked to provide a photograph of the Farnborough main runway for a publicity publication. The interesting aspect was that the picture should be taken from the centre line of the runway looking along heading 07 some 10 ft or less above the runway, from an aircraft in flight!

I took a young lady expert photographer in the right hand seat of the CAPIO (Charlie Zulu) and did two or three runs. It was quite exciting. She had a split second to take the photograph. Two copies of the shots are illustrated.

There have been interesting occasions at Farnborough. A nurse student after take-off turned insufficiently cross-wind. I asked her where she was going. She replied, "the airfield has moved!" A student in response to my request to change fuel tanks on return to Farnborough at 1500 ft over Fleet turned the fuel off. I just managed to keep the engine going after a rapid check; I asked him to move his knee so that I could see the fuel selector. I called "put the fuel on", he replied, "which tank?!!"

In 2002 I became Chief Flying Instructor at Farnborough taking over from Squadron Leader (Dr) Mike Bagshaw. Probably Mike is the best instructor in the UK. Another book would be needed to describe all of his history and phenomenal achievements.

I was surprised to find that I had been pilot mostly P1 (Captain) on some 50 odd types and major variants. Together with all types flown at RAE etc and passenger flying it totalled some 144 types. And to think that my Mum would not let me have a five bob flip in the 1930s.

As an examiner I initially examined for only ground examinations but eventually qualified as a flight examiner. Under the arrangements of the CAA UK PPL until circa 1997 I did several General Flight and separately the Navigation Flight Tests. However these tests were combined when the Joint European arrangements came into being under the overall title of Skill Tests. Up to January 2003 I have done 54 tests. Of these only 4 or so failed but after re-training and retest gained their PPLs. Instrument Meteorological Condition ratings both initial and revalidation tests have been a regular feature of my flying. Additionally there have been Proficiency Tests for those whose revalidation had run out. Altogether I seemed to have more testing of the JAA pilots and students than anyone else to date, at any rate for an examiner in his 80th year. The question of age has meant an eagle-eye cast in my direction by the medical people. My wonderful friend and examiner Mike Bagshaw has been a tower of strength in this regard. The official system however seems to pull the plant up periodically to see if the roots are OK.

The flying at White Waltham has produced one or two interesting occasions. Some years ago in the 1970s, an Ercoupe suffered a cracked exhaust. I suffered Carbon Monoxide poisoning. I was flying solo and before passing out managed to land, more or less by drill numbers. I

xl - Avions Mudry CAP 10B, Freddy's favourite mount.

Low level over Farnborough's main runway, 1985.
(Crown Copyright MoD)

had a bad headache for days.

Cherokee 180 G-AVSC had an engine failure at 50 feet on take off. The student had not put the front fuel drain into a completely safe position after testing for water. Actually there was no need to do that test; he had not told me that he had done it. I got down just short of the airfield hedge.

By my 80th birthday I had completed 51 JAR Skill Tests, qualifying students for a Private Pilot's Licence. Each student invariably demonstrated the quality of his or her instructor. I have found that many women make very good pilots, although some tend to underestimate their own ability.

In 2002 (April – May) I did skill tests for Chris and Ricki (17 and 16 years of age respectively). I judged them to be the two best examinees that I have tested so far at the time of writing. The 2½ hour long tests were taken in their stride. The young learn quickly and do not have the inhibitions of older people. They both did the test with no faults. One had not even completed the minimum 45 hours and we had to extend the test to enable him to get sufficient time for a grant of a JAR/PPL; i.e. the European Standard.

Flying in cloud, especially doing an instrument landing system approach has twice produced a student with a loss of control caused by disorientation. The first time resulted in a spiral dive in cloud. Just on the 'never exceed' speed I got control some 12 seconds before we hit the high ground. On another occasion we stalled with 40° of right bank. The recovery was over corrected and we descended, still in cloud with hard left bank. Recovery in cloud and cessation of the exercise was safely completed with the help of Sarah in Air Traffic Control at Farnborough.

Chapter 13

RETIREMENT WORK

When I retired in June 1982 at the age of 60, I felt that, up until that date, I had been frantically busy running the largest division, the Cockpit Research Division, Flight Systems Department, in the Establishment. I was concerned that it would be like dropping off a cliff going from extremely busy to nothing. I went to Tom Kerr just before my farewell functions and asked if he had any ideas. He told me about his plans to make a civil enclave of the airfield for business aviation. He offered me the job of helping a team to set it up. This involved completing lease arrangements in conjunction with seven local councils, the MOD, land agents and others. I was offered accommodation in the headquarters building *Q101.

I was made Secretary of the Liaison Committee and had a very frustrating number of meetings with representatives of the seven local town councils. Many of the members were sceptical of the civil aviation development of the airfield. The RAE Secretary, Dennis Blazye, was Chairman of the Committee. At the time of writing complete development of the airfield under the TAG Company is under way and the airfield has been leased to them by the Ministry of Defence..

When the work began just 20 years earlier the south part of the enclave was occupied by Southern Squadron, RAE with crews in the old ETPS building. This became the terminal eventually with Carroll Aircraft Corporation and other sub contract companies in the offices. However, Southern Squadron left early in anticipation of immediate introduction of the civil units; it was indeed too early. I had looked after the safety of the building for two or three years while it remained empty.

I spent five years helping our Director at Farnborough, Tom Kerr. Firstly adviser to Tom and the RAE Board, but also as a member of the team setting up the Civil Enclave on the airfield. This was to transform the airfield into a Business Aviation Airport. Other work involved the completion of some of my work before 1982. One job was to transfer a Chinook simulator from Scotland to the Flight Systems Department, in fact my old division.

I was pleased to get into ˙Q101 Building and had an office on the fifth floor. I was given another personal assistant her name was Jean, in keeping with five predecessors.

Among my jobs was the training of scientists and apprentices to fly. The hours of instruction were given at Farnborough and Bedford.

During the 1970s the apprentices at RAE Bedford had reconstructed a Piper PA28-140 Cherokee aircraft from a badly damaged state to flying condition with a full public transport licence. Because I had an instructor

xli - PA28-140 G-ATJG. My aircraft when attached to Transport Flight RAE in 1987. It was used for scientist and apprentice flying instruction and was built from salvage by the Bedford apprentices.
(Crown Copyright MoD)

rating, I was asked by the RAE management to give selected apprentices at both Farnborough and Bedford, ten hours of flying instruction, all of it dual. The aircraft G-ATJG was in excellent condition when I was given it. Initially I flew it at Bedford, enjoying the long runway and a complete change of scenery. I then took it to Farnborough and was attached effectively to Transport Flight under the wing of Sqn. Leader Fred Hambly, who also had a civil instructor rating.

On occasion I would ferry the aircraft to and from Bedford in difficult weather. If the aircraft was left at Bedford, I would travel as a passenger in one or other of the Transport Flight Devons, or later their Chieftains.

I painted the scene soon after landing back at Farnborough one evening in a Devon. I memorised the view as we passed over the Woodley NDB near Reading. It is included here.

I had to follow the strict routines of RAF service operating signing Forms 700 and attending the 8 am Met briefing parade in Air Traffic Control.

The students were variable in ability as might be expected. As a pilot one must learn various periodic tests while flying. One such test, remembered by a mnemonic is FREDA:

F for fuel contents and pressures

R for radio frequency etc.

E for engine, temperatures and pressures, carburettor heat control

D for gyro direction indicator check

A for altimeter setting check

A shortened version is LIFE:

L for location and look-out for other traffic

I for instruments

F for fuel

E for engine

While flying with a student at Bedford, I reminded him to do his LIFE check. He did not respond, I asked him again without result, when I asked him "why are you not doing your LIFE check?" he replied, "I have forgotten how to spell LIFE".

Sadly, upon the closure of the RAE apprentice's school, G-ATJG became redundant. In spite of my efforts to get the RAE Aero Club to buy it without success, it was sold to a German buyer for around £10,000. Perhaps I should have bought it myself.

I was invited to join the Board of Carroll Aircraft Corporation and I was given an office in the old Empire Test Pilots School (ETPS) Building. At one time I shared a room with that great Chairman, Air Marshal Sir Ivor Broome. Sadly he died in 2003.

It was such a pity when the Carroll establishment went into liquidation. Many people had enjoyed the facilities, especially the hospitality chalet at the Farnborough Air Displays. The chalet was a stand-alone two storey pre-fabricated building with a superb view of the airfield. It was furnished somewhat exotically, even the stair carpet had the Carroll motif woven into the treads. I had been made curator of the Farnborough Carroll Art Collection. Many paintings and artefacts were displayed including a lot of my paintings. The collection was broken up with the liquidation of Carroll Aircraft.

As president of the local Multiple Sclerosis Society, I was pleased to welcome our members on two occasions. Wine and food was abundant. One very welcome visitor was Arthur English; he was an Aldershot and Farnborough resident of world renown. We knew each other well and I am so pleased that we had some good companionship before he died.

I retired officially on 14th June 1982 as mentioned elsewhere. However, due to my being re-employed part-time, I was retired and remustered annually thereafter, so I actually retired five times. On one occasion two

xlii - Air Marshal Sir Ivor Broom, Wing Commander Ray Lomas and FSS in the Carrol Aircraft Pavilion.

letters arrived at home in the same post. One letter said goodbye, the other welcomed me back. I thus served 45 years before going to Carroll Aircraft.

While at Carroll, RAE gave me some contracts. One was to search the Establishment at the main base, at National Gas Turbine Establishment (NGTE) and Bedford to discover and list any stored important scientific or engineering equipment for historical retention. I made a complete dossier and passed it to the Chief Engineer. I have no idea what happened to it subsequently.

I also had to examine and identify, then record the subjects of a large number of glass photographic slides collected from the old Cardington station. The photographs covered from 1915 to just before Word War II. The results were catalogued and published in book form and distributed to all of the main museums.

During my year as Master of the Guild of Air Pilots and Air Navigators (1989-90) I was asked by Wing Commander (later Group Captain) Roger Gault, to paint a picture for his squadron of the Harrier aircraft of No. 4 Squadron RAF based at Guttersloh in Germany. The Squadron would be on exercises in a forest using a metal runway for take off and landing. I flew in a commercial transport to Germany before beginning an interesting road journey to the exercise site. I arrived in Wellington boots at the end of the forest at dusk. I was challenged by service personnel as guards from camouflaged posts several times. The men had machine guns.

*xliii - **Ivor Broom and Group Captain John Cunningham.***

After a long walk through the trees, out of the gloaming, came a figure, also in gumboots. He called "Master"! A great greeting from the Commanding Officer. He showed me around and we bedded down in a bivouac at a late hour. At 4.00 am I was awakened by the loud speaker system calling "Reveille, Reveille, it's 0400 hours!" Immediately the jet engine of a Harrier broke into song on test. The ground crew had worked on it overnight.

The Harrier flying from the short metal runway among the trees was exciting. When I received all the data I needed for the painting I was flown back to Guttersloh in a Puma helicopter. Airmen in full battle kit with sub-machine guns accompanied me, but the most interesting member of the team was a young woman, in full battle kit, with a sub-machine gun!

Back at Farnborough I heard that one of the Black Sheds near South Gate had been demolished and the second might go. Both sheds had been built circa 1915. From 1919 to 1937 they had housed No. 4 Squadron. I contacted Roger and he arranged a Harrier exercise from Germany to the UK. Upon arrival at Farnborough, two aircraft taxied to the front of the remaining hangar being used at the time as the fire station. I arranged for a selection of photographs to be taken, one showing the young officers, the aircraft and myself as illustrated. No. 4 was back home.

For several years my great friend Dr. (Sqn Ldr) Mike Bagshaw was Chief Flying Instructor of the RAE Flying Club. After two stints in the

xliv - Visit by No.4 Squadron in front of the 'Black Sheds' August 1990. (Crown Copyright MoD)

job, he resigned as CFI but remained a member. With the change of RAE into DERA the Club changed its name but remained the Royal Aircraft Establishment Flying Club Plc.

One of my jobs in the RAE Flying Club was, as mentioned earlier, to scatter Sheila Scott's ashes over Thruxton from the RAE Cherokee 140. Fred Hambly flew with me and we let the ashes go from the open door of the aircraft at low height over the airfield. I had packed the ashes in a Kenco tube and let them stream out as a dust. I felt awful, despite the cold, the draught and the extra noise as the remains of that great aviator streamed away. Fred handled the aircraft while I let the ashes go.

Some years later (2002) I was asked by a close friend, Frank Dell, if I could do a similar ashes scattering for, again, someone special.

A few words about Frank. He had been a Mosquito pilot during World War II. He was shot down over Europe and crash landed. He escaped and was picked up by the Resistance, in Holland I believe. He joined them and assisted in sabotage against the Germans. When allied forces advanced into his area, Frank was sent out into the open to speak to a tank crew to introduce himself and his friends. He clearly hoped that the tank crew were not trigger- happy.

Frank returned to the UK and became a commercial pilot rising to senior Captain British Airways. He became a Master of the Guild of Air Pilots and Air Navigator, in fact the year before me. He is a leading member of the Escaping Society. It was in that role that he approached me to learn if I could scatter the ashes of an erstwhile French Resistance member, a lady called Madame Suzanne Charisse.

Suzanne has been the subject of a book. Ken Charisse, son of Suzanne, requested that, to meet his mother's last wishes, she should have her

*xlv - **Master and Mistress of The Guild, 1989.***

ashes scattered over the English countryside. It took some time for me to get exemption from Air Navigation (No. 2) Order 1995 (Article 116) to drop an article from the air. See Appendix A

I dropped the ashes over Watership Down, which seemed a good idea. I had to get permission from the owner of the land, Andrew Lloyd Weber. His manager arranged authority. It was only because I do voluntary work

xlvi - The Grand Master and The Master.

with the police at Farnborough that I was able to trace the landowner through the local constabulary in the Watership Down area.

Suzanne Charisse was one of the last of the girls to be trained by the SOE and she hardly needed training because she had been active already with the Resistance forces for four years. Through imprisonment and hardship and at the end of her resources she had been rescued by the Royal Navy and brought to England in 1944. As a slim blonde of seventeen she started her own resistance group with youngsters her own age.

xlvii - HRH Prince Philip - Grand Master with Master and Wardens.

After unsuccessfully attempting to reach England to join the Forces, she went to Paris. There she helped British soldiers to escape. In January 1943 Suzanne was captured in Lyons by the Gestapo and was subjected to terrible treatment for two months before being sent to a hostage prison at Castres. She stayed there from May to September. She was selected to be shot but with a group of other prisoners, managed to escape. Her story in full is truly amazing.

As I watched the dust escape from the Kenco tube into the slipstream of Kilo X Ray, our aircraft, seeing it float towards Watership Down, my heart was very full, thinking that such dust was indeed that of a very brave and gallant soul. I thanked God for such people.

During my year as Master of the Guild, I was delighted to get to know Wing Commander Ray Lomas, the senior instructor navigation at RAF Finingley. As Master I was delighted to attend a presentation guest night and present a Guild Trophy to the best graduate of the school.

At a Guild visit to the airfield, I was given the opportunity of flying in a Jet Provost on a two aircraft low level simulated attack on a bridge on the Scottish borders. After much attention by staff who fitted me with immersion kit and all of the paraphernalia concerned with flight in a modern jet trainer, I was allocated a P2 seat with a Squadron Leader. On take off he asked me if I had ever flown a Jet Provost before. On saying "no", as we climbed he said "It's all yours" and I had control. Keeping up with No. 1 ahead of us was not easy. He suggested that instead of playing

*xlvii - FSS painting for Mike Bagshaw - his favourite Hawker Hunter
T Mk7, XL563, over Farnborough.*

tunes with the throttle, I should keep station by using the air brake. My
first attempt was the feeling of hitting a brick wall. As we thumped our
way over hilly terrain at about 500 ft, I began to find the tight fitting kit,
oxygen mask, bone dome and ejector seat straps quite uncomfortable.
We were 12 seconds late at the bridge, but we made it.

On return, just on finals, ATC told us to "go around" for traffic reasons.
The discomfort period was enhanced. Renée was on the apron awaiting
our return. She said I looked green. I am sure it was just discomfort
of the kit.

I was commissioned by the Officer Commanding RAF Lyneham to paint
a picture of the Hercules aircraft on the airfield. I was given an enormous
amount of help. He gave me his staff car for the exercise with WRAF
driver. As we sat on the apron, and as I sketched in the car, officers and
NCOs came to the car to ask questions of the CO. They were surprised
and puzzled when they saw what was really going on; he seemed pleased
with the picture, reproduced here. I included himself awaiting the arrival
of VIPs to the station.

In 1997 I was surprised at the award of the UK Instructor of the Year
trophy by the Aircraft Owners and Pilots Association. Much of this according to the supporting commendation was for keeping the RAE Flying
Club going over the years. A couple of years later I was grateful to receive
the Guild of Air Pilots and Air Navigators Award of Merit Medal, this time
for services to aviation. How I wish that Renée could have known about it.
Our friend Jenny came to see me receive the medal presented by Prince,

xlix - Raymond Baxter -
Commentator at GAPAN.

Sam presents the prize.

later King Abdullah of Jordan at the Guildhall in the City of London. It all reminded me of the time years before when I received the Freedom of the City of London, prior to be installed with the Guild Livery.

1989 my year as Master of the Guild coincided with the Master's Garden Party. I decided to have it at White Waltham. The day turned out to be glorious, in fact very hot. A good turnout was entertained by a comprehensive flying display. I opened the show with a fast low level fly past in front of the crowd along runway 03. I did this solo in Charlie Zulu. I was followed by a stream of aircraft either flown by a past master or at least having a past master as passenger. The last one in stream was a Mosquito. The show included some spectacular aerobatic displays. A highlight was the arrival of a Harrier from No. 4 Squadron in Germany. It landed among clouds of dust on a metal mat, installed the day previously by the Royal Engineers.

The party commentator over the address system was Raymond Baxter, well known to us all, and one of the Guild. The catering was served in an inflatable tent, coloured blue and white. As mentioned it was very hot. When a waitress plugged the tea urn into the mains, the fuse blew and the motor driving the tent inflation system failed. The tent slowly deflated with the dignitaries enjoying tea, rushing to exit. I heard one was a pregnant lady not looking for that sort of entertainment.

A spot landing competition winner was awarded a bottle of wine. Raymond announced that my young grandson Sam would present the prize. I noticed that Sam had been taken quietly on a side for a briefing by one of our Liverymen. When Sam eventually looked up at the tall pilot winner, he was heard to say over the address system, "I could have done that!"

l - Chipmunk G-BDDD.

li - Lizzie Bagshaw and FSS.

It was a wonderful day, but will always be remembered for the collapsed tent.

Early in 1992 Mike Bagshaw taught me how to fly at night. I did the normal 5 hour course and then went to Blackbushe to get the night instructor rating with Laury Adlington who had examined me for instructor revalidation and my IMC instructor previously. I have enjoyed teaching at night. One gets a remarkably cosy feeling with all the lights below.

Amusingly on a Friday night at 7 pm I would turn the ADF onto the lowest frequency available i.e. 200 kc/s or kilohertz as they say now. I could switch on the ident and hear the 'Archers' on Radio 4 of the BBC. The ATC was still quite clear when the controller spoke. Friday night

*lii - **Landing at the Bruntingthorpe fly-in, 2002.***

usually ended the broadcast with an exciting climax. On one occasion my student complained that the Archers was distracting him although his night flying had reached a good standard and his course was almost completed.

On occasion Air Traffic Control (ATC) at Farnborough would ask me to do a simulated emergency during a circuit. This would exercise the emergency services. The arrangement was made over the telephone before flight so that the 'Practice call' would alert the system without warning. I did two exercises. One in the Chipmunk G-BDDD and the other with a student from White Waltham doing a practice ILS approach. On that occasion he was pleased to land to get Farnborough in his logbook.

The Chipmunk exercise required me to turn onto a taxiway from the main runway, then switch off the engine. I was surrounded quickly by what seemed to be a fleet of vehicles. Ambulances, fire engines and small vans. I was lifted out of the aircraft and laid on the ground. The fireman put an oxygen mask over my face and said "What is your problem, Sir?" I said "I'm drunk". This took him aback but it was all taken in good part. On each occasion after the rescue vehicles had driven away, I was left to restart the engine of the aircraft. On each occasion I took ages to get it going much to my embarrassment.

On 15th June 2002 I celebrated my 80th birthday with a party at White Waltham. I invited over 100 guests and began the show with a low level fly past at fast cruising speed down runway 21, solo. Before that I took all four grandsons flying in G-BOSE Charles Godfrey's Archer aircraft. It was good to introduce my friends to each other and to have the CFI, David Coe, Mike Bagshaw and Ron Elder, Head of Flight Crew Licensing Civil Aviation Authority speak and present me with a life-long certificate and a model of the Piper Super Cub G-WLAC in which I convert pilots to the art of tail wheel aircraft handling.

Chapter 14

WONDERFUL PEOPLE IN MY LIFE

Tom Kerr, who was my Director at RAE in the late 1970S and early 1980s, also Director of NGTE and Director General in /MOD, brought me the gift of his book on 14th October 2002. A painting of the Fairey FD2 which I had done for him some ten years before was on the back cover. Tom's kindness reminded me of the enormous part he had played in my professional life, as the SPSO in charge of the Cockpit Research Division at RAE and the way he employed me as an adviser to him and the RAE Board of Management, of his giving me the role of setting up the Farnborough Airfield Civil Enclave and other tasks. Some of this I record elsewhere in this book.

All of this made me think of those wonderful people who influenced my career positively throughout my life.

The main guide and help was firstly my wonderful wife, Renée, who always supported me and never, and I mean never, let me down. Anyway the professionals however, starting during World War II, they were –

Leonard Bounds in 1943/44 who effectively lifted me from the lowest grade of Laboratory Assistant to a Technical Grade and who gave me responsibilities well beyond my actual position.

Caradoc Williams who helped me gain a lot of experience in navigation and propagation with a lot of trust in me; helped by Albert Brown before he migrated to New Zealand, as did Caradoc.

Walter (Johnnie) Johnson my Division Leader 1956 – 60 who gave me so much encouragement and trust. He recommended me for the lift in the Double Promotion from Experimental Officer to Senior Scientific Officer and put me up for a flying training course, which gave me the opportunity of taking up flying instruction and flight examining up to the time of writing.

Then of course there has been Mike Bagshaw, my dear friend who has helped me for years as my Aeromedical Doctor and as a pilot and examiner. Also a wonderful friend to Renée and me. He and Penny stayed with Renée and me until half an hour before Renée died.

I owe so much to my Dad, I have always been proud of him, as a soldier and a supporter of everything I did. He was such a good friend. In his later years he flew with me some 200 times and loved Renée and Carol too. He loaned me enough money to see us through the building and purchase of Beverley Fair, and acted as our guarantor. He was a great father and husband to Mum. He clearly loved Ivor too. Those who knew him in the Regiment and elsewhere treated him with admiration.

One dark evening I stood with him on the front lawn of Beverley Fair. We looked up and saw the bright pinpoint of light as an earth satellite

liii - 15 June 2002, my 80th birthday party, during which I flew PA28-108 Archer G-BOSE.

crossed from West to East. He said that so much had changed in his lifetime. From horsedrawn transport when he was young, from dirt to tarmac roads. From army uniform only recently to khaki from red tunics. All of that to the change to radar, supersonic flight, television and modern technology.

This made me ponder about changes in my own lifetime. From that day in Victoria Barracks, Beverley on the swing, looking up at the biplane. When there was no television, crystal radio sets only, no central heating and gas lights in the flat. This through the era of valve radios, the introduction of transistors, the microchip avionics, infra-red, fibre-optic cables, mobile phones and the huge development of aviation.

My schoolmaster Brindley Thomas set me up both at Aldershot and Farnborough in terms of giving me encouragement to take on the responsibilities at the Grammar School. In fact many of those wonderful teachers were so supportive. No wonder I enjoyed it all so much.

As I struggle with exercises in the gym three or four times a week to stay fit enough at 81 to retain my Class 1 JAR pilots licence; with its several medicals a year, BP tests treadmill exercises to near exhaustion and ECGs, Thallium tests etc; the magic of flying and being a pilot remains vital to the fulfilment of life itself. I thank the Good Lord that he gave me those gifts.

Chapter 15

THE CHURCH AND PAINTING

Life at St Peter's Church, Farnborough, the Old Parish Church has provided a great background to it all. I first attended there in 1937/38 when I was in digs in Highgate Lane. During the war we had church parades there. After Carol was born I became a sidesman, then for nine years, was Churchwarden, becoming Churchwarden Emeritus since then. Carol was christened there, Renée and I were married there. Both Renée and Carol were confirmed there and all of our parents and then Renée had their funeral services in the church.

I have been fortunate enough to assist with a team each August, since 2000, providing retired people with two days of interesting talks and activities. It is interesting to note how some manage to find lots to do in later life. Some just don't bother. I have found voluntary work most rewarding, particularly work in collaboration with the police. Operating from the Farnborough nick I have co-ordinated some 104 Neighbourhood Watches. Also it has been challenging to deal with young offenders as one of the local Appropriate Adult team. The youngsters in our Church who are quite amazing in their dedication to Community Service, compare starkly with the unfortunate youths who break the law. The latter invariably come from broken homes and have had little to stimulate them except crime.

I began painting when we were in Washington. By 1962 Renée and I were getting a little bored with the frequent round of Embassy parties and entertainments. There was little one could do to meet the requirements of hobbies which we had back in England. I tried doing a bit of painting and drawing which had its origin under Mr Foster at the Grammar School. I started with water colours which were pretty awful. The subjects were varied but the results disappointing. When we got back to the UK, I was introduced to both oils and acrylics. Results were much better but oils took too long to dry since time for painting was limited. Acrylics were exciting however and suited aviation subjects. Around 1970 I met the wartime artist Roy Knockolds. He introduced me to the Guild of Aviation Artists and gave me much valuable advice which has stood me in good stead over the years. I exhibited at their exhibitions and sold some. I became a member of the Guild of Aviation Committee and at one time arranged their accommodation in the Guild of Air Pilots and Air Navigators offices in Eccleston Street, London.

After getting pictures published in some calendars and on the GAPAN Christmas Card, followed by cards for the Tiger Club, things expanded. I have been pleased to have been commissioned by people in the USA, Australia, Germany and all over the UK. Although I enjoy aviation painting I love seascapes, animals and landscapes. Painting the sea is exciting,

liv - 'Woodley Inbound' The RAE Transport Flight DH Devon returning from Bedford - by FSS.

the patience required is so great until suddenly it comes to life and one feels that you have achieved ones aim.

Having met Terence Cuneo, Frank Wootton, David Shepherd, John Young, Mike Turner and Roy Knockolds, I always have a standard to aim for. My best picture is always my next one.

Painting, especially aviation subjects has been a fulfilling paying pastime. I am so grateful to the management at White Waltham for giving me the 'snag' in the historic club building as an art gallery.

I have also been pleased to have had a selection of paintings in the terminal building of the Civil Enclave at Farnborough. These pictures formed part of the Carroll Aircraft Corporation collection when I was the curator.

This book contains nine reproductions of some of my paintings which are inserted in the appropriate text. Those subjects which have been commissioned have highlighted some event, aircraft or subject forming a special place in the recipient's heart.

When I do a commission for someone, they usually ask how long did it take. My answer is '45 years'. My best picture is always my next.

Since the age of fourteen I have built models of aircraft, many from scratch as mentioned elsewhere. As one grows older the question of a resting place for some 350 models, particularly the inter world war period 1920-1940, gives cause for concern. Most are British types of aircraft, with the emphasis upon historical subjects.

The greatest gift to all is life itself, which needs to be lived to the full. Fellowship and the love of those near to one are a vital part of that full living. For some of the years since Renée died, our love of animals has been continued by the arrival of my dear cat "Toffee". He knows all my secrets.

It has all been, and is still, such fun.

lv - RAF Lyneham by FSS.

lvi - HS125 G-BRMC over Farnborough. FSS painting for Ready Mix Concrete.

lvii - 'Toffee'

MEMBERSHIP OF PANELS AND COMMITTEES

There are many memories of Committees and Panels I have been so fortunate to enjoy. I list them here probably as an apology to other members for leaving them out of the main narrative of my story. My thanks are extended to all who may find their particular interest included.

Guild of Air Pilots and Air Navigators – COURT

Guild of Air Pilots and Air Navigators – Light and Executive Aircraft Committee

Guild of Air Pilots and Air Navigators – General Purposes and Financial Committee

Royal Institute of Navigation – Council Member

Royal Institute of Navigation – Chairman General Aviation Sub Committee

Royal Institute of Navigation – Membership and Fellowship Committee

General Aviation Safety Committee

Guild of Aviation Artists – Council

RAE/DRA Aero Club – Council Member (CFI and DCFI)

Royal Aeronautical Society – Avionics Panel

Royal Aeronautical Society – Board

CAA Cockpit Research Committee

UK Liaison Officer – Avionics Panel, AGARD – NATO

(Advisory Group Aircraft Research and Development)

Various St Peter's Church Committees, Parochial Church Council etc.

GAPAN Future Policy Committee

President Guild Flying Club

Chairman London Branch, Prince of Wales Regiment of Yorkshire Association (East and West Yorkshire)

President. The Multiple Sclerosis Society, Farnborough and District Branch

Neighbourhood Watch Coordinator for Farnborough

Chairman – The Guild Future Policy Committee

AWARDS

UK/AOPA Instructor of the Year 1997

Guild of Air Pilots and Navigators. Award of Merit Medal 1998

RADIO DEPARTMENT
ROYAL AIRCRAFT ESTABLISHMENT

TECHNICAL PAPERS WRITTEN
BY
F.S. STRINGER

(Unpublished RAE Report Data)

A Report on the Flight Trial at RAE to determine the Velocity of Radio Wave-Propagation *March 1949.*

Tests to Determine the effect of a Cathode Follower on the Performance of an Aircraft Whip Aerial at Low Frequencies *July 1949*

An Account of Experiments on the Comparative Performance of Suppressed and External Loop Aerials for the British Radio Compass (A.R.I. X303A) *October 1951*

Interpretation of Atmospheric Noise Data between 1 and 1.0 Mc/s for the Principal World Noise Zones. *January 1952*

Comparative Trials of a Suppressed and a Mast Aerial for the Decca Navigator Airborne Equipment in the Presence of Ionosphere Reflection. *April 1952*

Proposals for a Method of Pictorial Presentation to assist Interception Navigation of a Distance Bearing Radio Aid to Navigation *Issue I - May 1952. Issue II - February 1953*

An Account of Experiments to Determine the Homing and Direction Finding Performance of the British Radio Compass (A.R.I. X303A). *March 1953*

A Simple Aid to Interception Navigation for Fighter Aircraft Under Broadcast Control Conditions. *May 1953*

Information Relating to the Decca Navigation Installations in Aircraft of Wireless and Electrical Flight, Royal Aircraft Establishment. *July 1953, August 1953*

A Proposed Radio Aid for the Navigation of Short Range Light Weight Interceptor Aircraft. *December 1953*

A Technical Assessment of the suitability of the Decca Navigator as an aid to Fighter Aircraft Navigation. *April 1954*

A Visual Aid to Interceptor Navigator for Fighter Aircraft operating under Broadcast Control Conditions. *March 1954*

A Review of Long Range Radio Navigation Systems for Aircraft. *September 1954*

TACAN Navigation System

An Interim Report of the Flight Trials at The Royal Aircraft Establishment of the First Development Model ARI X1354. *June 1955*

The Flight Evaluation of the Tacan Airborne Equipment ARI X1354. *August 1957*

The Performance of Aerial System X9026 in the Valiant Aircraft. *August 1957*

A Centimetric Aircraft Aerial Radiation Pattern Measuring Technique using a Ground Radar. *August 1957*

An Interim Report of Centimetric Aerial Radiation Pattern Measurements using a Model Victor Aircraft. *August 1957*

An Interim Report on the Siting of Three Centimetric Jammer Aerials on the Vulcan Mk II Aircraft. *October 1957*

The Performance of Aerial System X9026 in the Victor Aircraft. *May 1958*

The Application of a Double Spiral Aerial to an R.C.M. Problem on the Vulcan Aircraft *February 1959*

Report of a Visit to H.M.S. Falcon, Halfa, Malta. *August 1959*

Interim Report of a Visit to USA and Canada on the subject of broadband E.C.M. Aerials *November 1959*

Report of a Visit to the Working Party Conference of the Committee on European Airspace Co-ordination (C.E.A.C.) on 3/4 December 1959, *December 1959*

Final Report of a Visit to the USA and Canada on the subject of Broadband E.C.M. Aerials *February 1960*

Report of the TACAN, DMET/IFF, SSR Compatibility Discussions and Demonstrations held in the USA, March 1960, *April 1960*

Centimetric Jammer Aerial Radiation Pattern Measurements on a Model Vulcan Aircraft. *May 1960*

The En-route Navigation System for the early Concorde Supersonic Transport Aircraft *February 1964*

The En-route Navigation System for the early Concorde Supersonic Transport Aircraft. *July 1964*

Report on Doppler/Losan A Observations on BOAC Flight to and from New York. *May 1964*

A Proposal for a Navigation Aid for use by Helicopter and Light Aircraft in the Support of Independent Combat Units. *September 1964*

Floating Platforms in the North Atlantic. Their use as Bases for En-route Navigation Aids. *November 1964*

Research and Development Philosophy as related to the Navigation of Transport Aircraft *January 1966*. (Also summarised in Flight Magazine October 1966)

A Proposed Deployment of VOR/DME in the London Terminal Control Area for Implementation in the Period 1966-1975. *March 1966*

Report of a Visit to the USA - 30 April-5 May 1966. *July 1966*

Differential Omega as an Aid to Tactical Navigation. *November 1966*

A Limited Assessment of the AN/ARN-88 Omega Receiver. *April 1967*

Notes on a Meeting of the NATO Sub-Group 2 of AC/235. *March 1967*

Omega : the Phase Modulation Technique of Resolving Ambiguities, Flight Trials to Barbados – August 1966. *January 1968*

Anglo-French Working Group on Electronic and Guidance Technique AFCP-13. Chief Liaison Persons Meeting. *March 1968*

Omega : Visit to the Omega Project Office (PM-9). Washington DC February 1968.*April 1968*

The Extension of the Long Range Aircraft Navigation System to the Short Range Role. *April 1968.* Also presented as a lecture to the Institute of Electrical Engineers, London March 1967 and the French Institute of Navigation.

Radio Navigation and the Strike Attack Aircraft. *May 1968*

The Omega Navigation System Experiment to Determine the Optimum Radiating Format for Ambiguity Resolution. *September 1968*

Omega, Flight Trial to Barbados – April to May 1968. *January 1969*

Omega : A Commentary upon Ambiguity Resolution for Aircraft Navigation. *July 1968*

A Long-Range Navigation System Extension Over the En-route/TMA Interface *October 1967*

Aircraft Navigation in the Future Role of Radio Aids. *January 1969*

The Navigation of Aircraft over Complex Terminal Areas. *October 1968*

Omega : A Worldwide Navigation System. *February 1969*

Also presented as a lecture to the <u>Institute of Electrical Engineers.</u>

Hyperbolic Radio Navigation Aids. *August 1969*

The TMA Role of Hybrid System Radio Sensors. *September 1969*

Navigation and Traffic Control in the 1970s. *January 1970*

Report on the Final Phase of the RAE/FAA VLF Navigation Study.

A Commentary upon Aircraft Navigation Systems

The Navigation of Light Aircraft. *circa 1970*

Anglo-Netherlands-Norwegian Co-operative Programme

Visit to the Norwegian Joint Signals Services, Oslo January 1969. *February 1969*

Given to various Universities on behalf of the Institute of Electrical Engineers Subject:- Electronics, Its future in Navigation.(Newcastle, Dublin, etc.)

<u>Lectures to Various Rotary Organisations</u>

The Church

British Airways Christian Society

The Multiple Sclerosis Society, Farnborough and District Branch

Visitors to the Carroll Aircraft Corporation

RAF Cranwell

Units visiting RAE

FLIGHT SYSTEMS DEPARTMENT, ROYAL AIRCRAFT ESTABLISHMENT
FSF (2) COCKPIT SYSTEMS DIVISION   1982

DIVISION HEAD – F.S STRINGER S.P.S.O
P.A. – Mrs J. Morgan

Advanced Cockpits   **Simulation**

Tel Ext.				Tel Ext.	
2511	R.G. White	PSO	3240	J.G. Mabberley	PSO
4331	Dr. G. Rowlands	PSO	3298	Dr. L. Bonnett	PSO
2515	D. Jarrett	SSO	3249	E.D. Whybray	SSO
2732	D Barter	PTO II	3483	A. Karavis	SSO
4322	Mrs B. Henderson	HSO (P/T)	3065	Dr. A. Cooke	HSO
2732	J.M. Barrett	SO	3483	K.W. Lord	HSO
3062	M. Hughes	PTO III	3345	N. Benger	HSO
4333	C. Ellis	ASO	3253	H.F. Hemmett	SO
4332	D. Knowles	CFT I	3065	P. Gatling	SO
2654	R. Bray	W.G. CDR	2909	G.S. Corner	PTO II
3617	D. North	S/LDR	2265	K.S. Pett	PTO II
2456	A. H. Husband	S/LDR	2094	D.E. Litten	PTO II
				A.D. Alner	CFT I
				P. Saville	CFT I
				A. Roberts	CFT I
				E. Pattison	EN I
				P. Langridge-Barker	EN I

Electronic Displays

Tel Ext.		
3069	A. Brown	PSO
2984	Dr. J. R. Banbury	PSO
3978	Dr. G. Jones	SSO
3232	S.H. Jones	SSO
3183	R. Shiel	SSO
3983	F.B. Whitfield	SSO
3232	K. Austin	SO
2980	Miss Bird	EN III
2980	D.N.Jeans	CFT I

COUNTRIES VISITED

Scotland	*	Ireland	
Wales	*	Denmark	*
France	*	Madeira*	
Germany	*	Corsica	
Switzerland		New Zealand	*
Spain		Hong Kong	*
Gibraltar		Belgium	
Portugal	*	Capri	*
Italy	*	Ibiza	*
Greece	*	Corfu	*
Turkey		Majorca	
Holland *		Minorca*	
Norway			
Sweden			
Lebanon			
Malta		St Lucia	-
Azores		St Martin	-
Bermuda	*	San Juan	-
Peru		Aruba	-
Ecuador		Sardinia	-
Chile		Curacao	-
Mexico		St Thomas	-
USA (30 States)	*	Iceland	-
Hawaii	*		
Fiji			
Samoa			
Australia	*		
New Guinea			
Guam			
Japan			
Aleutian Islands		* Accompanied by Renée	
Canada	*	- Accompanied by Carol	
Newfoundland			

LEARNED AND OTHER SOCIETIES MEMBERSHIP

The Guild of Air Pilots and Air Navigators. Master 1989-90 Joined Circa 1960

The Royal Aeronautics Society - Fellow. Various Committees

Chartered Engineer

The Royal Institute of Navigation – Fellow. Member of Various Committees and Chairman of Light Aviation Committee. One time Member of Council

Chairman Guild Flying Club, President in 2002

Churchwarden and Church Warden Emeritus. Churchwarden 9 years

DRA (and RAE) Flying Club. Chief Flying Instructor

The Farnborough and District Multiple Sclerosis Society – President

The Prince of Wales Own Regimental Association, London Branch – Chairman

The Army Air Corps Association. NE Hampshire Branch – Member

The City of Aviation Artists – Associate Member

The Royal Society of Arts – Fellow

Neighbourhood Watch Co-ordinator

Appropriate Adult Team Member (NE Hants Police and NCH)

PAST MEMBERSHIPS

The Tiger Club – Check Pilot

West London Aero Club – Instructor

Wiltshire Flying Club Thruxton – Pilot

Blackbushe – Instructor

NATO-AGARD (Research & Development) UK. Panel Avionics

British Embassy Washington DC USA – Member of Defence Research Staff

Radio Department Royal Aircraft Establishment

Flight Systems Department RAE. Head Cockpit Research Division

Assistant Director Extramural Research (Avionics) Farnborough

Assistant Director Extramural Research (Ministry of Defence Procurement Executive)

Advisor Director and Board RAE Farnborough

Director (Non Executive) Carroll Aircraft Corporation

Renée's Memberships

NAADFAS- National Association of Design and Fine Arts Society

Church Flower Guild (St Peter's Church)

Divorce Counsellor

Adult Literacy Teacher

Farnborough Technical College (A Levels)

Flower Petal Post

Considerable interest in Gardening, Pottery and Cooking – with much experience and knowledge of them all.

VIDEOS

In 1998 I was approached by Peter Frewer, a colleague in the Civil Enclave, to see if I would join him in participating in the production of a film concerning the history of research and development of aviation at Farnborough. Peter was Aviation Manager for TAG McLaren, based at Farnborough & Woking. He was an ex-RAF Pilot, who served in the night/all weather role flying Meteor and Javelin aircraft, before moving to Transport Command to fly Comet 4's and VC10's. During this period he flew several Royal Flights, including the Queen's visit to South America in 1968.

He subsequently joined Shell Aircraft Limited at Heathrow, flying HS 125 and Gulfstream aircraft.

We had talks with a film company based in Farnham called Onyx. I was made Technical Adviser and helped to provide a lot of material for the script and I introduced the team to many people who had played a significant part in the work at RAE over the years. They included Col. Cody's great grandsons and many of the past test pilots at Farnborough and Bedford. Gathering these wonderful people together was tremendous. Many who came for interview were eminent scientists including my old Director Tom Kerr. It was very rewarding to be joined by Group Captain (Cat's Eyes) Cunningham and Captain (Winkle) Brown.

Filming caused much amusement. The first sequence involved the view of a young boy (supposed to represent me) looking at the airfield from where I stood in the 1930s. His dress was completely wrong but the film Director said that was immaterial!

Early sequences involved me flying the Club Chipmunk G-BDDD with a cameraman in the rear cockpit. I was a little worried when the compere referred to me as the oldest instructor in the country. I had to point out the old RAE site features and the airfield. The only way I could do that was with the Chipmunk wing tip. The cameraman did a grand job despite the fact that the wings were nearly vertical at times.

The funding of the exercise caused the Onyx Company a lot of concern and we made visits to a variety of well-known figures, including Lord Norman Tebbit to elicit support. The film was produced and launched by DERA; i.e. the successor to RAE in the new Establishment to the west of the airfield. It was a splendid occasion and the film was shown on television by ITV in a six week series on Tuesday evenings for half an hour on each occasion: The film and video are entitled 'Above and Beyond.'

Later I was approached by another company based in Cardiff called 'Raw Charm.' I participated in that but mainly as an interviewee talking about my own experiences at RAE. I have never seen the result but I have been told by many people at White Waltham that they have seen it on Sky TV. That film was called 'Wings' and concerned the history of aviation in the south of England.

Appendix G
Civilians in Wartime

Subject:- <u>Attendance at G.H.Q. Home Guard School</u>.　　27H/HG/L/15/G.

The Director,
　R.A.E.,
　<u>Farnborough</u>.

　　　　May permission please be granted to 2nd Lieut. F.S. Stringer
for leave of absence from 21 - 27 Nov 43 (both dates inclusive) for
the purpose of attending a course at G.H.Q. Home Guard School, Dorking.

　　　　　　　　　　　　　　　　　　　　　　　　　　　　　　　　Major,
　　　　　　　　　　　　　Commanding, 27th Hamps Bn. Home Guard.

The Boltons,
19, Alexandra Road,
Farnborough.
17 Nov 43.

Copy to:- 2/Lieut. F.S. Stringer.

Subject:　　Course No. 1. G.H.Q. H.Q. School.

From:　　　O.C. 'A' (Farnborough) Coy.
　　　　　27th Hants Bn. H.G.

　To:　　　2/Lt. F. S. Stringer.　　　16th November, 1943.

　　　With reference to your nomination for the course
at the above school or 21st November, 1943. A copy of
the joining instructions is also attached.

　　　　　　　　　　　　L.P. CAUSTON.
　　　　　　　　　　　　　Major.
　　　　　　　　　O.C. 'A' (Farnborough) Coy.
　　　　　　　　　27th Hants Bn. H.G.

JOINING INSTRUCTIONS FOR STUDENTS ATTENDING NO. 1, G.H.Q. Home Guard School.

Address "Denbies" Dorking Surrey. Telephone 2765 Dorking
MR. 1 inch OS. (England) Sheet 124, 594696.

Railway Station. Dorking Town or Dorking North (S.R.)

Time and day of assembly 1800 hours, Sundays.

A. Students on arrival at the times above mentioned will report to the orderly room and fill in the arrival book.

B. Students will be required to share rooms. Beds, mattresses, blankets, and pillow slips are provided, but no cupboard space is available.

C. Students should bring with them mirrors, towels, soap cleaning material and may bring their own bedding if they so desire.

D. Batmen are not provided and will not be brought to the schools.

E. Cheques cannot be cashed at the at the schools, and drinks and mess charges will be paid for in cash.

F. Subsistence allowance will not be admissible as rations are drawn.

g Railway warrants will be provided by students' units for the journey to and from the schools.

H. Students will wear battle dress for all parades. A suit of denim overalls, and a greatcoat of mackintosh and a spare pair of boots or shoes will also be taken on all courses except those for Home Guard battalion commanders, training officers, and adjutants.

I Civil or military identity cards will be taken.

J. A mess charge not exceeding 1. 6d a day will be charged to cover extra messing, breakages and the provision of furniture glass and crockery newspapers and other amenities.

k. In the case of attendance at courses lasting for at least six days, if loss of earnings is sustained, compensation up to a maximum of £3. 18. 6d a week and 13. 1d per day for odd days is admissible, subject to a deduction of 1.6d a day for food. Where it is necessary for a member of the Home Guard to travel to and from the school on the day before, and the day after the course and he loses his normal earnings on these days, a claim for compensation without deduction for food will be admissible. When compensation is admissible, travelling allowance under A.C.I. 1442 of 1941 or any amendment thereto will not be payable. Claims will be submitted by members of the Home Guard to their units; the forms set out as Appendices A.C.I. 2006 of 1942 will be used for this purpose.

HOME GUARD TRAVELLING WING PROGRAMME
2 JULY - 4 July, 1942
----

2 July

TIME	SUBJECT
1000 - 1030	Assemble: Security etc.
1030 - 1110	Grenades. Part I
1110 - 1120	Break
1120 - 1230	Observation Tng: Short Talk Scheme I
1230 - 1400	Lunch
1400 - 1440	Grenades Part II
1445 - 1520	T.M.C.
1525 - 1545	Sten M.C.
1545 - 1700	Observation Tng Scheme II and III
1900 - 1955	29 mm Spigot Mortar & Bombs
2000 - 2100	-do- -do- Drill and Practice

----

3 July

TIME	
1000 - 1045	Street Fighting I
1050 - 1130	Fieldcraft
1130 - 1150	Break
1150 - 1230	$2\frac{1}{2}$-inch Disch: 36 and 38 Gdes
1230 - 1400	Lunch
1400 - 1545	29 mm Spigot Mortar Firing Practice
1600 - 1700	Message writing and practice
1900 - 2100	Use of Ground: Stalks, etc.

----

4 July

TIME	
1000 - 1045	Patrols General
1045 - 1120	Street Fighting II
1120 - 1130	Break
11.30- 1230	Coaching on the Firing Point
1230 - 1400	Lunch
1400 - 1700	Patrol Exercise
1900 - 2015	Camouflage and Concealment
2015 - 2100	Principles of Instruction

Subject: N.C.O's Cadre Course No.2

From: O.C. 'A'(Farnborough)Coy.   70 Netley St,
            27th Hants Bn. H.G.   Farnborough,
                                                Hants.
To: Sgt. Stringer, F.S,
            No.4 Platoon.   22nd July, 1943.

            The following is a copy of the report
regarding your course.   You should show this to
your Platoon Commander.

Attendance   Max. 24.   24.

Keenness   Very keen.

WEAPONS

        General Knowledge   Very good.

        Tactical   Very good.

        Siting   Sound.

Tactical Knowledge   Very good.

Remarks   Very capable leader and
                                     instructor.

                        [signature]

                        Major,
                        O.C. 'A'(Farnborough)Coy
                        27th Hants Bn.H.G.

BATTLE PLATOON ORGANISATION. NO. 4 PLATOON.

1. No: ....

Pte: .... Your Squad is No: .... Your

Squad Commander is Cpl: .... and your second i/c Squad

is L/Cpl: .... Your Squad post is No: ....

The Battle Pl. posts are Nos. 1, 7 and 12.   Check their location
with your Squad Commander immediately.

If you go to action stations you will draw your extra ammunition
then report to your Squad Commander, at your Squad post.

2. The Battle Pl. consists of:-

Pl. H.Q.................... Pl. Commander, Pl. Sgt. Runners, E.Y.
Rifleman. (Sniper when necessary).

3 Squads.................. Normally consisting of Squad Commander,
2 i/c Squad, Nos. 1 and 2 Riflemen, Nos.
1 and 2 Bombers and Nos. 1 and 2 B.A.R.
Group.

N.C.Os. normally carry Stens. Bombers carry rifle or Sten.

The 2 i/c Squad is issued with an E.Y. rifle, he may however give this
to a member of the B.A.R. group in action.

The B.A.R. group are the Light Machine Gun Group and have a Browning
Automatic Rifle.   The 2 i/c Squad is in charge of the B.A.R. Group.   As
a Browning is not available for all three squads. No. 3 Squad only will be
issued with one.   Rifles or E.Y. Rifles will normally make up the B.A.R.
groups of Nos. 1 and 2 squads.

3. Whenever you parade with the Battle Pl., unless ordered otherwise,
always carry your personal weapon, wear a steel helmet, webbing and denim
overalls if issued.

4. Our operational role as Battle Pl. is

(i) To defend the posts allocated to the Battle Pl. in the defended
locality (D.L.) in the event of a concentrated enemy attack
on the district.

(ii) To reconnoitre the area and clear any small enemy parties within
a certain radius of the D.L.

(iii) To act as a counter attack force in the D.L. subsequent to
any post being taken by the enemy.

5. In order to carry out the above tasks you must be proficient in battlecraft,
the use of your weapons, know your locality and be able to act as part of a
team in the squad and Pl. flanking attacks and wood clearing parties.

Keep this copy in a safe place.   Learn Paras. 1 to 4 by heart.

CAMOUFLAGE OF 29 MM. SPIGOT MORTAR.

IF NO NATURAL BACKGROUND EXISTS
AN ARTIFICIAL ONE MUST BE PROVIDED.

SIGHT LINE *MUST* BE KEPT CLEAR.

LIGHT GREEN

YELLOW

S.C.C. 1a

COUNTERSHADING ON FRONT
OF SHIELD.

BOMB COVERED BY TOW
B.G OR OTHER LIGHT MATERIAL

CULLACORTS
WIRED ON

UNDERSIDE OF
BARREL COUNTER —
SHADED.

CULLACORTS
WIRED TO
SHIELD

NATURAL MATERIAL OR
STEEL WOOL MAY
BE USED TO BREAK
CIRCULAR SHAPE OF PIT.

DWG. BY W.J.G.
"G" (CAM)
H.Q. E.C.

CONCEALMENT OF WEAPONS.

LIGHT AUTOMATIC AND CREW.

A PIECE OF WIRE NETTING WITH A SPIKE AT EACH END TO BE GARNISHED WITH SCRIM KNOTS

LOCAL MATERIAL TO BE ADDED ON SITE.

2'-3"

6"

4'-0"

SCREEN MAY BE ROLLED UP FOR TRANSPORT.

USE OF FACE VEIL.

GARNISHED WITH KNOTS OF HESSIAN TO COVER FACE & RESPIRATOR WHEN OBSERVING.

WHEN NOT IN USE IT CAN BE FLUNG BACK TO REDUCE SHINE OF GAS CAPE AND PACK.

ARTIFICIAL FOLIAGE

CULLACORTS — FEATHER NETTING

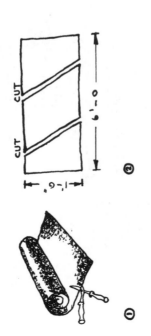

CUT

CUT

6'-0

1'-6"

③

①

WIRED TO BRUSHWOOD

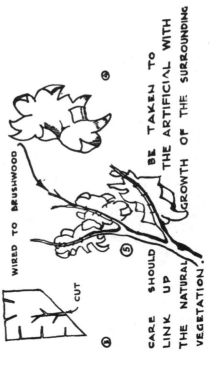

CUT

⑥

④

⑤

CARE SHOULD BE TAKEN TO LINK UP THE ARTIFICIAL WITH THE NATURAL GROWTH OF THE SURROUNDING VEGETATION.

Appendix H
Dropping Articles from the Air

FAX

Tel: Farnborough (01252) 545990
MOBILE 0378 001756

Mr. Mike Wood,
General Aviation Branch
Civil Aviation Authority.

FAX 01293 – 573510

Beverley Fair,
21 Revelstoke Avenue,
Farnborough,
Hants
GU14 8NG

7 October 1999

Dropping of Ashes from the Air.

Dear Mike,

Further to our recent telephone conversation, this is to confirm that I have been asked by a senior member of the Escaping Society to seek permission to drop the ashes of Mrs Shorwise over the English countryside. She played a significant part in helping our airmen escape from France during World War II. Her wish was to have her ashes dropped over England.

I performed a similar task once before some years ago. The following permission by the CAA is sought therefore.

To fly PA28-180 G-BBKX from Farnborough on or about 20th October (depending upon good VMC) over the area south of Kingsclere ie. approximately 5 miles NW of Basingstoke. To fly at 600 ft agl and deposit the ashes. I would use a safety pilot (probably an ATPL and GA instructor).

Do please contact me if you require any further information.

Yours Sincerely

Freddy Stringer.

F. S. STRINGER
UK/FE (PPL) 202264H
CFI DERA Aero. Club
Farnborough.

7 November, 1999

Dear Freddie,

It is some time now since you very kindly carried out my mother's last wishes, and I have had time to ponder on the past difficult months and the effect both on myself, my family and particularly my father of my mother's unexpected and very sudden death. It meant a great deal to me that, not only were her last wishes fulfilled, but they were fulfilled by someone whom I am certain she would both have respected and liked.

I was very pleased to have the opportunity to meet you, and to find the impression gained on the 'phone reinforced. Your compassion, thoughtfulness and real desire to perform the task in the best possible circumstances were entirely what I would have expected from our conversations. I found you to be someone who fully understood the importance and value of carrying out my mother's wishes in a dignified manner and at an appropriate location, which I know you chose only after careful consideration. I cannot express my gratitude strongly enough for what you did, and the manner in which you did it. My only regret is that we had to meet under such unfortunate circumstances.

Ideally, I would like you to meet my father as I believe you have much in common, but at present I do not feel he is ready for that. Perhaps in the future it might be feasible. Certainly I would like to keep in contact with you if that it all right with you.

I enclose a map of what I believe to be the area you used, and would be grateful if you could indicate on it the relevant section.

I hope you are well and still enjoying your flying.

Yours,

Ken Charisse